Dancing
Between the
Opposites

A Daoist Guide to Balance and Self-Cultivation

Craig Mallett

First published in 2020

First Edition

ISBN: 978-0-6488566-0-3

Editing + Proofreading by Cavalletti Communications, www.cavacom.biz
Cover Design and illustrations by Pelin Korkmazel, www.behance.net/pelinkorkmazel
Author Photograph by Jimmy Logue, www.jimmylogue.com/
Typesetting by Luke Harris of WorkingType, www.workingtype.com.au
Printed in Australia by Ingram Spark

Disclaimer
The material in this publication is of the nature of general comment only, and does not represent professional advice. It is not intended to provide specific guidance for particular circumstances and it should not be relied on as the basis for any decision to take action or not take action on any matter which it covers. Readers should obtain professional advice where appropriate, before making any such decision. To the maximum extent permitted by law, the author and publisher disclaim all responsibility and liability to any person, arising directly or indirectly from any person taking or not taking action based on the information in this publication.

 A catalogue record for this
work is available from the
National Library of Australia

Efforts have been made to contact the copright holder for permission
to use the image on p100. Please contact the author to discuss this matter.

Table of Contents

....

Acknowledgements

....

The origins of this book are quite peculiar, as it is a book that has almost written itself – as if by some sort of cosmic accident. It started as a handbook, only a few pages long, that I would give to my online students so they could have some theory framing the exercises I was giving them. As my experience with this format of teaching grew, so did the contents of this document and it started to span more and more pages. Simultaneously, I was writing regular blog posts on my website which I would also send to my students as 'required reading' homework. At some point, I made a decision to paste the text from the blog posts after the theory in the handbook so it was all together and new students would not have to go digging through my website's archives to access all the information necessary for their development.

One day when looking over all the information I had collated, I realised there was a consistent theme, a reasonable number of words, and what appeared to be a start, middle and end. 'I don't get it, what exactly do you teach?' is a question I am often asked, but one that has been perpetually difficult for me to answer in a single sentence or two. Without context and a point of reference, what I do seems outright bizarre. A book had suddenly appeared in front of me that could provide this point of reference. It needed a lot of tidying up and some new writing to link it all together, but it had definitely taken shape as a book – one I had never intended to write!

As I near completion of the manuscript, I look back with gratitude to all who made this series of fortunate events possible. First and foremost, I must thank my wonderful wife Cherie, and my parents, who have given me their unconditional love and support as I dived into many weird and wonderful rabbit holes of research and went through many awkward phases of development. Next, I must give my heartiest thanks to the Da Xuan tradition and my teacher, Serge Augier, whose teachings brought structure and clarity to my practice and search, and are a constant source of inspiration and awe-filled mystery. I must also offer my deep thanks to all those outside of the tradition who have had a significant impact on my development: my first teacher Wang Laoshi, for teaching me many wonderful things and starting me on the Way; Simon Thakur of *Ancestral Movement*, Kit Laughlin and Olivia Allnut of *Stretch Therapy*, Dave Wardman of *Physical Alchemy*, Emmet Louis of *Motion Impulse*, and Adyashanti of *Open Gate Sangha* – who each shared teachings with me that will be with me for life; all of my students (past, present and future) without whom I am just a rambling idiot on the street talking to myself; and my dear friends Eamon, Bendy Dave, Robbie, Will and Michael. Finally, I must thank my editor, Jessica Stewart, for helping me transform this manuscript from a series of random articles into a coherent book!

Craig Mallett
Brisbane, Australia | February 2020

Foreword

....

I have known Craig for many years now and I am very proud of his work in our tradition. When I met him for the first time, he was still working a regular job and hadn't yet gone deep into the training of the tradition, but I could see his dynamism and enthusiasm. I found him to be very humble and eager to learn, despite his already great knowledge acquired in his previous training. Soon after we met, he really went full force into the training and worked hard to imbue the teachings into his life. I am very pleased to see the progress that he has made over his many years of study, practise, research, and travel. He is open-minded both in learning and sharing his knowledge and now he has succeeded in making his first book about the Da Xuan tradition. Making this knowledge available to the world, so that all people can practise, learn, improve, and enjoy a higher quality of life together, is invaluable. Through his persistence, patience, and humility, he has set a very good example for the new generation to follow.

The book is very clear and informative – it's a seamless bridge from mundane life, to questioning, to a daily practice for spiritual evolution. We need more people working towards their own spiritual growth and building a better world for tomorrow.

This book is perfect for understanding the fundamental aspects of our evolution. We are responsible for the future and it will be the result of our conscious efforts to wake up and to grow.

Serge Augier
Heir and Guardian of the Da Xuan Daoist Tradition
Paris, France / *February 2020*

Introduction

....

cultivate

[kuhl-tuh-veyt]

verb (used with object), cul·ti·vat·ed, cul·ti·vat·ing.

- *to promote or improve the growth of something by labour and attention*

- *to develop or improve by education or training; train; refine: to cultivate a singing voice*

- *to promote the growth or development of (an art, science, etc.); foster.*

How It All Began

Ever since I can remember, I have had two big urges motivate almost everything I do. The first is that I've always had an impulse to get to the underlying truth of things. My mind has a tendency to immediately go meta, and if someone were to show me a new way of doing something I would question why it's done that way, and look for hidden elements that connected it to what I knew of the bigger picture (or set it apart). The second urge is a drive to be of service to other people and the world. While this has expressed itself in unseemly ways at times as I unskilfully or arrogantly forced my opinion on others, at the heart of this was a simple and innocent desire to help. This book is my way of being of service to my readers by sharing what I've discovered so that it might assist them in their own path of self-cultivation.

I like the big picture, so let's start there. In my search for the underlying truths of things, I began to notice currents of habits, behaviours and motivations that appeared to drive everything we do. I enjoyed the simplicity found in viewing the world in this way and loved learning about the obvious physical and behavioural patterns, or more subtle and intricate habits of belief, of myself and those around me. What I found is that some habits are very useful, others are useless but harmless, and others still are quite malicious. Whatever their quality, I have been compelled by some unknown force to learn more about them and how to bring balance to my life by understanding them. I felt it important to become more aware of the currents of my life so that it wouldn't fly by with me on autopilot the whole time.

The image of a person in a canoe navigating a mighty river comes to mind. Whether full of chaotic rapids or appearing to calmly flow along for a while, it is always in motion. It seemed to me as though some people were adamant in exhausting all of their strength paddling upstream against the current, and others were content simply not paddling at all and letting themselves be thrown about and smashed into whatever obstacles appeared. The skilful and balanced option would be to learn to read and feel the currents, paddle strongly when necessary to put yourself in the best position for the river to carry you, and otherwise relax and enjoy the ride; a perfect combination of exertion and relaxation. I wanted this kind of skill for my life so I had to learn about the currents of life and methods of paddling so I could navigate them with more finesse.

More simply put, I just want to know how I work, and where possible improve upon it. Even in my youth, well before engaging in any formal practices, I often played little games with myself to help me notice the currents that played out in my personality and my life. Over the course of a couple of decades doing this, I feel that I can finally share something that will be more useful than it is confusing. It is something that has called me in some way or another since the very beginning of my life, so some tales of how it all began seems like the proper place to start.

FIRST STEPS

Rewind to circa 2003 ... I was a young 17-year-old who had just moved out of home and across the country into the frozen (well, burning at the time actually) plains of Canberra, the capital of

Australia. I was reasonably active in my youth, playing soccer first, then field hockey for many years as well as being involved in Korean Karate. I had always enjoyed a good martial arts film but had never been immersed in the legendary Bruce Lee culture that many others with interests in the Eastern arts had. Rather, my nerdy opiates of choice at the time were computers and gaming. I had moved to Canberra to study 3D animation and special effects with hopes of one day becoming a game developer. With this desire came many, many hours of sitting at a computer annihilating virtual enemies while downing the nectar of my people: copious amounts of soft drink and junk food. One particular binge was responsible for the first turn away from this lifestyle and towards something more balanced. I clearly remember the scene – I was at my friend's place whose father had left on business for a few months. With no one monitoring us, we unleashed the full magnitude of indulgence in our addictions. Many days (or weeks?) passed as we gamed for most of each day and night, pausing only momentarily to venture to the shops to pick up instant noodles or order more pizza. In our haze, we viewed many of the viral videos of the time – this was pre-YouTube days and so videos had to be downloaded. One such video was black and white footage of a *Wŭshù* competition. Wushu is a modern reinvention of the traditional Chinese Martial Arts and was created by the Chinese government in response to a public demand for the return of cultural arts that had been outlawed during the Cultural Revolution. Its focus is gymnastic in nature, and like gymnastics, the competitors are judged for their form, presentation, speed, agility, and difficult acrobatic manoeuvres.

Something stirred in me upon its viewing. These people

displayed incredible ability as a result of their dedication and hard work, abilities which I had previously believed were only possible in the realms of fantasy and role-playing that my friends and I were so hooked on. We had been doing quite the opposite of what was necessary to get to such places in real life. We had grand imaginations, but lack of light, movement and proper food had degenerated us to pale (literally) imitations of ourselves, weak and sickly. The nerds of the early 2000s did not dare venture into a gym. Perhaps though, just maybe, we could train like the figures we saw in the video, learning to leap acrobatically through the air? One of my friends had lived in China for quite a few years and recalled that training in Wushu had been mandatory at school there and was extremely fun. We hit up the phone book and internet and found an ex-national champion of China was on our very doorstep teaching classes. In Canberra!?

We only lasted about a month in the modern Wushu classes, for we were immediately caught by something else. The teacher of the class had suggested that more training was better and that there was another more traditional class being run on the days that she wasn't teaching. Being keen and young we figured more training was a great idea and so we signed up there as well. It wasn't long before the curious wisdom of this other incredibly talented teacher (seriously – another one in Canberra??!?) completely enveloped us. We quickly dropped the modern classes and sunk ourselves fully into this traditional method.

Our new teacher's name was Wang Laoshi, and he would become my guide for the next decade. He was a lineage holder of several rare and strange looking styles of Chinese Martial Arts. *Xīn Yì Liù Hé Quán* (Heart-Mind and Six Harmonies Boxing) and *Chā Quán* (Cha Family Boxing) were the central styles we began with, later augmented by Yang family *Tàijí* (aka Tai Chi) that he had learnt from Fu Zhongwen. The Taiji was mostly to help us relax because we were too damned stiff. Both the former styles came from Wang Laoshi's extended family who were part of the Chinese Muslim community, known in China as *Huízú*. These styles were traditionally taught only to Hui Chinese, being kept away even from the other Chinese populations until the mid-twentieth century, so we were very lucky to be taught this material.

Wang Laoshi's focus was not on the martial aspects or the beauty of performance. He was interested in self-cultivation and classes oscillated between drilling motions up and down the hall and lectures on the philosophy of Buddhism, Daoism and Confucianism. Some part of this spoke to me deeply. I couldn't articulate how learning about oneself in this manner was different to any other pursuit of health like going to the gym or doing kickboxing or some such. But it was different. We were exploring deep topics. He would leave us with little sayings or poems that we were to consider and try to understand or express in our practice:

两心通 – Liǎng xīn tōng
十指连 – Shízhǐ lián
凌风击掌 – Líng fēng jīzhǎng
润心田 – Rùn xīntián

Through two hearts
Ten fingers connect
Threatening the wind with the strike of the palms
To nourish the field of our heart

~Zhang Zhaoyuan
(Wang Laoshi's teacher)

What did poems like this mean? How do you nourish your heart by striking your palms against the wind? The teachings were all very alien and us students struggled to understand what Wang Laoshi was trying to deliver. But even in my failure, something persisted. Nihilism was not my style, neither was surrender. I was more on the side of naive romanticism – there was a hidden treasure locked behind what he was conveying, a taste left in my mouth that I was determined to find the source of.

THE GRIND

I never did discover what these mysterious puzzles meant in my time with Wang Laoshi. My practice regularly being taken off the burner to go drinking and partying certainly didn't help, and there was also a tangible communication barrier as he struggled to relate to us and his newly adopted culture. The Chinese ways of whacking us with a stick to keep us in our stances or getting our parents to chastise us for missing practice were not open – he had to find other ways to motivate and entertain us extra-relaxed, lazy Australians. There was occasionally an air of sadness or defeat around him as he shared stories of the farm boys he taught in China whose skills far surpassed even the most dedicated students of the Australian class.

As the years wore on my training turned from novel to routine, and the cushy government job I had at the time compounded the problem. Weeks, months and years passed and my lack of focus meant that the only changes I saw were minute improvements in my physical skills and not much else. So, in 2011, I planned a six-month trip to China. I hoped that I could break out of the stagnation, train intensively and make the discovery I yearned for. But I returned defeated, just as stuck as when I left. A fond memory of being (correctly and justifiably) chastised after my return lingers: 'Craig has not even entered the front door yet.'

EXPLORATION

In the period that followed, I turned my gaze outward. Wang Laoshi closed his school at the end of 2012. Classes were too small and his new family and job kept him busy. He would always have time to meet with us and answer questions but it was not the same as regular contact in class. A few of us continued to meet at an oval and train as best we could. I had already began looking into various gymnastic strength training modalities, flexibility practices, natural movement frameworks and more. Perhaps what I sought lay outside my previously constructed borders?

I had returned to my government job, but I knew that it was not the place for me, and I wanted out. In 2012 I became qualified as a personal trainer and took up a part-time position at a local 'Globo-gym' type facility. I desperately wanted to teach people in the way I had been taught and add that intangible something else which had grabbed me in the beginning. This element evaded all my attempts to define it but, to me, was very clearly missing from the modes of practice and exercise I saw people participating in. I wanted to find a way to bring it out in what I taught, but the gym was not the right place to undertake such adventures and I did not have enough of a personal charge or depth of understanding of what 'it' was to pull it off. I struggled for a full year to convey the exercises and information, haphazardly mixing material from the martial arts I had learnt with stretching, strength work, movement practices, and more. Clients were few and I had made almost no inroads into understanding how to teach what I knew I had to teach during this time. While this period taught me very little of what to do, it taught me plenty about what not to do.

It was during this time that I also began teaching Natural Movement workshops around Australia and outdoor movement classes alongside Simon Thakur of Ancestral Movement in Canberra. I almost completely put away the material from Wang Laoshi at this stage, only occasionally showing something during a class for novelty or training myself for nostalgic reasons.

This was a fun period for me. I had managed to reduce my office hours to three days a week, and outdoor training and nature exposure quenched my thirst for a deeper connection. The dazzling lights of many different modalities of physical practice provided a significant distraction. I would lose myself down rabbit holes of infinite contemplation on any one of hundreds of topics. I trained in all the systems I could find that seemed to relate: Stretch Therapy and other flexibility training, Gymnastic Strength Training, Methode Naturelle, Parkour, acrobatic training and other calisthenics, hand balancing, re-wilding systems of all kinds, forays into Feldenkrais, Eugene Sandow's five pound dumbbell protocols, other martial arts like Shaolin Kung Fu, Theravadan and Zen Buddhism, the Movement Culture of Ido Portal, and a deep dive into an offshoot of Stretch Therapy called Physical Alchemy (created by my friend Dave Wardman). I spent hours training in physical practices from these systems most days. Complexity was my king and I served it by bringing as much to the table as I could find. And a mighty and complex collection it was indeed!

But no matter how expansive my knowledge became, it never fanned the flames of my heart. I knew deep down that the 'something else' was still missing but, on the surface, I continued pretending that it wasn't. The strong yearning for something bigger and deeper than myself slowly faded until the ember was but a speck, barely perceivable but still alight. Just.

A TURNING POINT

While trying to piece together some kind of Frankenstein-esque system of 'self-cultivation' from all the interesting things I'd learnt from these studies, a chance scouring of the web led me to a certain blog – the *Urban Daoist*. I swallowed the blog in its entirety. My internal flame flickered. This French man was talking about exactly the same topics that Wang Laoshi had taught, but with a Western cultural perspective. I emailed to enquire further. No response. How curious! I used every contact I had to try and get in touch, to no avail. Salvation soon showed itself, however – a new button appeared on the blog: 'Distance training in English now available'. I immediately clicked and signed up and became a student of Serge Augier and the Da Xuan Daoist tradition.

The tradition did everything I had been trying to do, only better. It was informed by more than 1,500 years of experience and the combined wisdom of all the great minds of the tradition. You might be able to imagine my surprise when I found out that the exact thing I was trying to create already existed!

The first year of training was sketchy at best. I was still quite immersed in the multi-disciplinary 'movement culture' and felt that I had somehow short-changed myself if I did not do my movement training even when I had practised Serge's material. And anyway, I knew it all already. It was obviously the same as what I was already doing and so I didn't really need to train it that much. I soaked up the theoretical material from the videos Serge sent me though – it would be a worthy addition to the collection.

I remember hesitating when I was coming up to the point of renewal into the second year of training. *I should probably just quit the training with Serge, after all it's pretty expensive and it's basically the same as what I'm already doing,* I thought to myself. Thankfully, some well-timed advice from my friend Dave (the previously mentioned creator of Physical Alchemy) helped me into a moment of clarity and I decided to renew after all.

The decision to continue with Serge marked another huge shift in my perception of things. My feeling of what was worthwhile and important in my practice changed dramatically – it was so tangible I could have almost grabbed it. It was as if a switch was flipped. Five hours of stretching, strength, acrobatics and more could be trained in a day and I would still feel as though I had done nothing. 'Normal' exercise felt the same to me as sitting around binge watching TV. 'Stop distracting yourself, attend to your practices!' And so, I did. I progressively discarded the scattered practices from here and there to immerse myself in a tried and tested tradition.

I could not pretend to 'know it all' any longer. Slowly I was exposed to more and more of the teachings and began to discover the deeper aspects of the school. It soon became obvious that more than a decade of training with some of the best teachers in the world had little carry over to the Da Xuan material and that I wasn't too far off being a clueless beginner.

COMMITMENT

As the years pass and I dive deeper into my Da Xuan studies and practices I find less need to look elsewhere to understand myself, my habits and my patterns. There are numerous topics in the school that go into all kinds of details about the way we function, why we are like this and what can be done about it. It requires a lifetime of dedication and fits my personal quest to the tee. My obsession with habits, behaviours and underlying motivations has let me enter and practise in the school with a unique perspective, for better or worse. Having significant experience in what *not* to do has put me on the lookout for the critical clues that would bring more light to the many mysteries that I had come across.

This brings us to now. I hesitated to write this book for fear that my interpretations of the tradition might be as askew as they have been in the past. Thankfully, my practice has pushed me to confront and overcome deep fears of not being worthwhile enough to embark on such a task; it has brought me a clarity of mind that helped me cut through the fabrications of a million 'what-ifs'. Time to just get on with it to see what happens. The icing on the cake came in the form of advice from my teacher, Serge: 'You need to explain things in a new way and share this as widely as possible. People want to hear what you've got to say even if you think they don't.'

So here we are, and what I've got to share has two parts. The first is my interpretation of some of the most fundamental concepts and practices from Da Xuan which will frame this journey of self-cultivation and provide simple advice on what to actually do to get started. The second thing I wanted to share is a collection of ideas that will serve to orient our approach and attitudes. Should you be interested in cultivating your own life in this way, the orientation and the attitude is the first port of call. It will set you up, reveal the first series of obstacles, and give you the choice of doing something about them if desired.

A WORD OF ADVICE

For anyone intending to join the tradition, or for those already in (hello!), always remember to check these concepts with your teacher who can tell you if they come as formal advice from the tradition or are my own interpretation. Make sure they are right for you.

For those outside the tradition, I will present here what I feel are the most useful elements that can be engaged with in a less formal way. Exercises and ideas that you can use for simple well-being, to help you out of a rut, or perhaps to assist you in the exploration and cultivation of your own path of practice. I've included Chinese terminology as a reference point for those who are already familiar with the topic or simply curious about such things.

I recommend trying out the practices for yourself before coming to a conclusion about whether or not you agree with what I'm writing or go off sharing the ideas with others (although please feel free to encourage them to get a copy of this book!). We Daoists are first and foremost pragmatic, and I would much rather have you discard all of it and never think of it again than run around throwing these ideas at unsuspecting bystanders without first having a lived experience of what the ideas are pointing towards. There is already enough of this happening in the world and I'd prefer not to add to it.

Understanding Tradition – Daoism & Da Xuan

Before we get into the nitty-gritty of it all, I have to remind myself that many of the people who read this book may not be familiar with terms whose meaning I take for granted. Let's start as basically as possible. If you search the internet for the term Daoism you will run into many differing explanations. The Chinese character is 道 – (pinyin: *dào*), and it literally means *'way'* or *'path'*. You will also often find the word written in roman characters as *tao* – it's a different spelling but refers to the same character and there is no difference in meaning here. I'm going to stick with the *dao* spelling for the duration of this book to keep things simple.

No two Daoist traditions are alike, even though they often refer to the same classical texts. There can be as much difference between Daoist traditions as there are between the various Abrahamic traditions that are all based on the Bible. There's little need to be a scholar on the subject to get on with practice but, to avoid confusion, there are a few things that need to be pointed out.

Daoist traditions were originally organised within tribes, families or clans from the region that is now China. Not unlike the various indigenous tribes and clans in the Americas and Australia, each group had their own set of practices and traditions to help guide them through the difficulties of life and live in harmony with the world. This collection of traditions, practices and philosophies were usually guarded by the village elders and shamans of each group (called 方士 *fāngshì* in Chinese; literally 'method master') and were passed down from generation to generation. As time went on and the traditions came into more regular contact with each other, they sometimes shared practices and adopted newly introduced ways that they liked or found a use for. A big shift came when the Indian traditions (*Buddhism* in particular) ventured north. Many Daoist sects followed the will of the people who liked the spectacle of the ceremonies and ritualistic temple life associated with these traditions. They broke away from the clan-style organisation to become temple Daoists, whose traditions are a mix of Buddhism and clan Daoism. The most well-known location for temple Daoism is Wudang Mountain, a name often referred to in the classic Kung Fu films of the 1980s and made famous when one of the most influential hip-hop groups of all time, the *Wu-Tang Clan*, borrowed the name. Most of the information found about Daoism on the internet today is drawn from Wudang or other lineages of temple Daoism, who are notable for their priest or monk-like robes and special hats.

However, many Daoist clans decided to keep the old ways and stayed amongst the world rather than withdrawing to the solitude of temple life. They continued to pass on their traditions as they had always done (often far away from the public eye), without the special clothing or buildings. In our tradition's own history, it is said that nine clans came together in 510 AD to create the Ba Men Da Xuan tradition (Chinese: 八门大玄, pinyin: *bā mén dà xuán*, literally 'Eight Gates [into the] Big Mystery') in an effort to pool their collective knowledge and save it from being lost to the ever-quickening pace of modern life. Since then, the tradition has continued to be passed on as the clans of the past did and is currently under the guardianship of my teacher, Serge Augier.

While not true of all Daoist traditions, Da Xuan is specifically non-cultural and non-religious. We are concerned with the development of *human* qualities and, as such, the practices are open to anyone of any culture or belief – you do not need to go to any temples or adopt any new belief structures. Practices on mindfulness, meditation, self-cultivation and so forth that originate in the temple traditions work fantastically in the temple setting but can be very difficult to adapt to modern life. Some people have varying success in adapting them, but many others run into dead ends. Following the clan way, Da

Xuan is a tradition *in-life*, which means that the practices work best and are specifically designed to be done by people who are in amongst the busy-ness and difficulties of family, work, socialisation and distractions of the mundane, everyday world. It's a wonderful thing to have the support of a tradition that has many centuries of experience dealing with how to make these practices work and find wholeness *within* the hardships of ordinary, non-temple life.

'Sounds good to me, where do we start?' you might say. Glad you asked, let's get into it!

Chapter 1:

A Framework for Personal Practice

....

framework

[freym-wurk]

noun

- *a skeletal structure designed to support or enclose something*

- *a frame or structure composed of parts fitted and joined together.*

Three Treasures

In all schools of Daoism, there is a concept called the three treasures *(三寶 sānbǎo)*. This is a trinity that works on many levels (and often described with different names depending on the context – see glossary for details). The sun, moon and stars; heaven, humans and the earth; and *Jīng* (physical essence; the body), *Qì* (breath/energy/vitality) and *Shén* (mind/spirit), are all examples of this trinity in different contexts. You find this trinity anywhere there are opposites – which is everywhere. You have the positive and negative opposing extremes, and the space in the middle that connects them and allows them to mix.

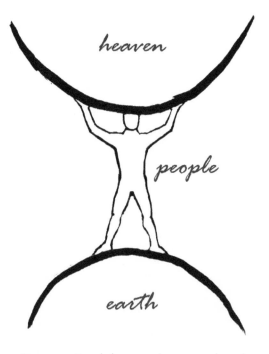

Figure 1 — People between heaven and earth

The creation story of Daoism tells us that from a field of infinite potential and primordial chaos (before opposites exist, *Hùn dùn*), space/nothingness is born (0 – *Wújí*). Once there is space, there can be something in the space (1 – *Tàijí*). Now there are opposites: nothing and something (2 – Yin and Yang). They start to mix and the three treasures arise: [nothing] + [transforming into] + [something] or vice versa (3 – Yin and Yang mixing and in motion). This mixing of Yin and Yang, the *Three Treasures*, go on to create everything that is manifested (often referred to in Chinese literature as 万物 *wànwù*, sometimes translated as the *Ten Thousand Things*). This creation story is less of a historical reference and more of a description of how every single moment occurs. In a very general sense, it refers to the extreme poles of any opposites and the centre/spectrum around or through which the opposites mix and transform into one another. *Dao* refers to all of this play of opposites and its source at once. A few chapters from the *Dào Dé Jīng* (below) show the importance of the trinity, the absolute source of the trinity that is called the dao, and the relationship we as humans have with the trinity and the dao:

> *The Dao produces One*
> *The One produces Two*
> *The Two produces Three*
> *The Three gives birth to the myriad of things,*
> *the Ten Thousand Things*
> *The Ten Thousand Things are made of Yin and Yang*
> *The way they interact with each other*
> *Creates Harmony*
> ~Dao De Jing Chapter 42*

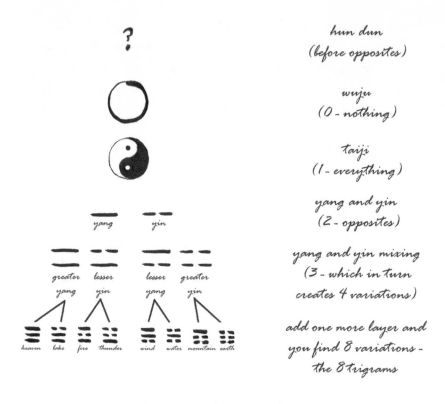

hun dun
(before opposites)

wuju
(0 - nothing)

taiji
(1 - everything)

yang and yin
(2 - opposites)

yang and yin mixing
(3 - which in turn
creates 4 variations)

add one more layer and
you find 8 variations -
the 8 trigrams

Figure 2 — Daoist creation diagram

As humans, we are in a special position: at the centre of the mix between the opposites. We are, with appropriate practice, able to have direct conscious experience of, and influence over both ends of the extremes: the divine heaven and the ordinary earth. We are also capable of connecting with and having *our own manifested experience* of the source of the opposites: the inexhaustible dao. All of this is possible for anyone who dedicates enough time to it.

There is an absolute which engulfs or
has everything inside it
It exists before Heaven and Earth
Without the names, without sound
Nothing depends on it nor does it depend on anything
It is inexhaustible
If in its acting in a circular manner
It cannot be exhausted
It is considered as the source of all under Heaven
I don't know its name, so I call it 'Dao'

If I have to call it some other name, I call it Absolute
So it has no limit and it acts everywhere
Acting everywhere it is omnipresent,
Being omnipresent, it's at the origin of everything
Dao is the absolute, Heaven is the absolute,
Earth is the absolute
But a human being is the absolute too

There are four great things in the Universe
And men are one of them
Men have to follow the path of Earth
Earth has to follow the path of Heaven
Heaven has to follow the path of Dao
And Dao follows its own nature
*~Dao De Jing Chapter 25**

translations by Serge Augier from the Da Xuan tradition

The table overleaf gives a few examples of the trinity at work within various contexts:

Table 1: Yin/Yang

Yang	Centre/Exchange Point (Yang and Yin)	Yin
non-manifested	becoming	manifested
heaven	man	earth
jing	qi	shen
mind	breath/circulation	body
mental	emotional	physical
spirit	energy	essence
divine	human	animal
extraordinary	human	ordinary
process	acting upon	structure
day	dawn/dusk	night
idea/thinking	put into	action/doing

Note that Yin and Yang are references to the way things change between opposites and are not static labels – you could very easily reverse the categorisation of many of the above depending on the context. It is a way to compare the opposites and, depending on what your subject is being compared with, will determine whether it falls in the category of Yin or Yang. Everything is in a constant state of transformation and fluctuation, and Yang and Yin are a way of comparing the positive and negative limits of this transformation respectively. They are two ends of a single whole, two sides of the same coin. To create balance is to keep the fluctuation between the limits fluid and smooth and not have it stagnate or get stuck at one end or the other.

On the human level, the body (*jing*) is constantly transforming into the mind (*shen*) and the mind into the body, by way of the breath and emotions (*qi*). The practices from Da Xuan that we will study in this book are designed specifically to encourage this circulation to continue and not become stuck at any stage.

To achieve this fluid balance in our lives, we have a fundamental concept that we need to follow: *no part of the trinity is of greater importance than any other.* Yin is not more important than Yang, Yang is not more important than Yin, and the mixing of Yin and Yang is not more important than the pure expression of either. One end of any extreme is not more important than the other.

Here we see our first practical and fundamental piece of advice that will inform the structure of our practice: the mind (Yang), the breath (Yang and Yin) and the body (Yin) are all of equal importance. It's all fine and well to say we think they are each equal, but the other side of this equation is what we *do*. If we spend two hours working on the mind each day, and only five minutes working on the breath and body then, by our actions, we are showing that we value the mind more than the body and breath. To strike a balance, each day we want to do something for the physical, something for the breath and energy, and something for the mind. The time given to each should be roughly equal.

We might also be able to see that most of our malicious habits are expressions of us being caught in one extreme or another.

It's like an old record stuck on loop, repeating a particular groove in the track. The groove is not the problem but being stuck in it is. We often need a little bump to get out, and organising our practice in a new, balanced way can provide this bump.

Alchemy

Our second practical piece of advice is the idea of simplification which comes from the alchemical traditions. In Western alchemy, the prime purpose of the experiments performed is to create an external transmutation that mirrors an internal shift. This is done by separating the materials into their most simplified elements (in the old language: salt [equivalent to *jing*], mercury [*qi*], sulfur [*shen*]), putting them through some kind of process to perfect each of the separated elements and then recombining them so they coagulate back into a slightly more perfected whole. The transmutations that happen in alchemy are not possible if the process of work on the base element is not correct, and it is also not possible to make the transmutation happen without separately perfecting the base elements in their simple forms first.

Without the separation and working process, you can still get transformations (as in modern chemistry), but they are not of the same order as those that can be achieved with this framework. Regardless of how cool a reaction you get in chemistry, you will never change lead into gold.

The pragmatic details (which exercises to do, how long for, and so on) will be revealed in later chapters, but first we must understand that if we want to commit to a practice that will balance us and bring about transmutation, it is necessary to operate in an alchemical way. Many of the exercises will seem unreasonably simple, but they are for good reason. We want to separate what we are doing into these super simplified base elements, perfect the element with practice and then success-fully recombine it into the whole. *Solve et Coagula* is the old Latin saying – dissolve and then coagulate. When this approach is used, we get results that are *more than the sum of the parts*. I have regularly encountered people who had a decent existing physical practice and meditation practice, sometimes for more than a decade. The meditation practice was almost always a combination of breathing work *and* focusing or watching the mind. In every case I have seen, even with such experienced practitioners, huge breakthroughs were made by separating their meditation practice into two more simplified pieces: one specifically for the breathing and the other specifically for the focus of the mind, both done every day.

In the beginning our practice time is isolated. We remove ourselves from the rhythms of normal life to work on each of the three base elements – *dissolve*. Practising creates certain qualities but it's not useful to only bring those qualities alive during our training sessions. We must bring the practice back and merge it with our regular, non-training lives – *coagu-late*. It won't work at first, but if we practise this cycle often enough, we can eventually find a real coagulation and progres-sively merge our training with our ordinary lives. To help this happen, the great majority of our practices are not too special or spectacular. Making our practice overly flowery – with fancy clothes, special locations, perfect smells and sounds, and big beautiful movements – sets up an expected environment for these qualities, isolating them and blocking them from arising anywhere else. While the spectacle can help establish practices and do other things, we have to understand that we put them there so we can eventually do away with them. We do spectacular things in ordinary ways to help the qualities 'leak' from our training times into the rest of life, uniting our practice with life.

Our practice is plain and simple to accommodate. The clothes we wear are our normal clothes, the places we practise are our home, local park, or even in the middle of the city or riding the busy trains. We mostly practise lying down, sitting, standing and walking, sometimes accompanied by simple motions of the arms and legs. Ordinary motions – up and down, forward and backward, stepping, turning the waist and so on. I joke that in the workshops and classes I teach, a bunch of people seem to be standing around not doing much, and video of my own practice would just show me doing ordinary life things like walking down the street, listening to my friends and family, and reaching to get things off a shelf. There is truth in jest though, and our hidden opposite, the extraordinary, lies inside every ordinary motion if we have practised enough.

Eventually, with enough formal practice, we find ourselves more often in informal and automatic practice and progress. We are easily aware of and use our circulation during these ordinary moments, keeping our alignment as we walk to the shops or sit down to watch a show, reaching for a cup with the coordination of the whole body, keeping our mind clear as we talk with our friends, actually maintaining focus on what people say to us, and so on. This feeds back into the formal training, making it more potent which, in turn, increases the potency of the informal part. As the unity grows, we find our training fuses more and more with our regular life.

In the beginning, these moments won't happen except in formal training. As alluring as it is to become a full-time practitioner, we have to be careful to not turn our life into a golden prison of formal training. We don't want to practise *instead* of living our lives or as a way of escaping the gritty, difficult parts of reality. Rather, we just do as much as we can while still living our lives completely. The secret is in keeping up the practice for the long term so that it has time to naturally infuse into the rest of life.

In our formal training we want to break our daily practice down into three distinct sessions so we can begin to perfect our three most basic aspects equally in their simplest forms:

1. Work on the *Shen (mind/spirit)*. These are practices where the intention is on the thoughts, concentration, or intention itself. Here we develop the qualities of the mind/spirit such as focus, concentration, mental relaxation, and meditation.

2. Work on the *Qi (breath/energy)*. These are practices where the attention is on the breath or the feelings of circulation or energy. Here we develop and regulate emotions and other exchanges using breath work, internal training (nei gong/qi gong), and internal alchemy methods.

3. Work on the *Jing (physical essence)*. These are practices

where the attention is on the posture and motion. Here we develop the physical body, repair the weak links in the structure, improve strength, alignment, grounding, relaxation and coordination.

Although qualities from all three categories are working in any given practice, we must put our intention completely on the aspect we are working on in that practice, so it may grow sufficiently. We must keep our attention away from the other two elements as much as possible. For instance, if we are working on the mind, we are working solely on the mind and not concerning ourselves with the body, breathing or sensations of energy and circulation.

Be very clear with what you are working on. During your physical practice, just get on with the physical practice and do your best to stay aware of the bodily elements. It's easy to get distracted by breathing when working on your posture or motion. One of the reasons for having the three practice categories is that you can rest assured knowing that you can come back later to work on the other parts.

We will look at exactly what to do in each of these categories in the next chapter, but first there is one more element to discuss that will help us train well.

Thresholds

The concept of *thresholds* is the third vital piece of the puzzle that will aid in our orientation towards practice, and I wish I had come to understand this idea much sooner than I did. I use the word threshold here because the experience of change that comes with this way of practice can be very sudden. It is as if you were walking towards a door of a strange house—the approach may be short or long—and then quite suddenly you pass through the door to transition from outside to inside and you are in a room you have not seen before.

As outlined in the previous section, in the Daoist approach to practice, we begin with very simple exercises. The fundamental exercises (some of which I will share in Chapter 2) are generally done lying, sitting, standing or walking, with some kind of motion of the arm or leg. Doing them once or twice is generally an easy affair and can be taught to most people in a short amount of time.

What is interesting here is that because we are practising in natural positions that we all use throughout our day-to-day lives, it is possible for even a rank beginner to do many of the exercises *sort-of-correctly* from the get-go. In my experience, however, people encountering this kind of practice for the first time commonly stop or interrupt their practice out of boredom, a belief that nothing terribly important is happening, or a feeling that they can already do the exercise correctly and so they are ready to move on to the next thing.

Doing the exercise 'correctly' here is not the purpose. In fact, to do the exercise correctly (in a general sense at least) is simply a sign that you have passed from learning *how* to do the exercise, to being able to get on with *doing* it. The point is not to do the exercise correctly, but to use the exercise to carry you towards and eventually beyond different thresholds. In a sense, it's closer to being able to begin training than being an indication of any kind of end. To do an exercise well does *not* mean you are done with the exercise – it simply makes it a more effective vessel for approaching whichever limits it is designed to address. It is also often the case that the threshold is not clear or obvious until after you've passed it.

The most basic physical thresholds are created by protective tension and in the course of my teaching, I have regularly witnessed people passing these tension thresholds for the first time. It is a wonderful sight to behold.

Typically, it goes something like this:

The exercise begins and all is good. Pretty soon the tension makes itself known; it is working hard and starting to fatigue. Burn, baby, burn! Slowly the feelings of fatigue increase, and the intensity begins to skyrocket. 'Oh god, it's only been two minutes and he said we are going for twenty?!?' The muscles burn and the blocked points feel as though they are searing into the skin. Just when it seems too much to bear, something relaxes. A burden melts away followed by great relief as the pleasant cool-warm feelings of circulation saturate the previously impenetrable walls of tissue. A look of bewilderment comes over the practitioner as they continue an exercise that moments ago was thought to be impossible to sustain any longer, but now proceeds with ease.

Sometimes the thresholds can be passed unknowingly. I recall one workshop where I was teaching to a group and a friend participating was talking of how pain in his knees amplified during the practices. Because we were standing upright, not taking any un-centred positions, I gently urged him on. In one of the sessions he continued to stand for well over an hour. Afterwards he told me how the pain in his knees had been quite intense at the beginning but then he became absorbed in the practice which had the intention directed towards the hands. At some point he realised that he hadn't thought about his knees for a while, and when he brought his attention back to them the pain had simply vanished without a trace and he was standing comfortably. It did not return.

This kind of moment is where potential can burst wide open. The practitioner now has their own experience of passing a threshold and so the 'threshold concept' transforms from a story they heard-but-didn't-really-believe, to a direct, lived experience. It is a moment where the practitioner can replace faith ('I don't know why I'm doing this stupid exercise but Craig said it will work so I better keep going') with certainty, inspiring them towards other challenging practices or deeper thresholds. It is also a moment where, even if you believed me consciously, you have now also convinced and trained your unconscious.

Training the unconscious is just as necessary to bring balance as training the conscious parts of ourselves. If we tell ourselves consciously that we are going to train a particular motion for ten minutes straight no matter what, and then give up the moment it gets uncomfortable, it's a way of succumbing to the will of the unconscious – a sure way to entrench yourself even further in your existing grooves. But if you do what you set out to do, even if it's a bit wonky and imperfect, then you not only send a clear message to your unconscious, but you also train your willpower to an incredible degree.

In the Da Xuan tradition we have a fantastic *Shen Gong* (mind training) exercise where you take a simple shape—such as a circle, square or triangle—of a single flat colour and stare at it for ten minutes or more. There's nothing more to it than this, no secret that needs to be told. Most beginners have considerable difficulty with it because, without fail, and often very quickly, it exposes mental and emotional limits, and as a result they think they are doing it incorrectly. On the contrary, this shows that the exercise is working perfectly and all that is needed is the willpower to sustain the exercise until the thresholds are passed. As with the physical exercises, the mind or the emotions can become very intense as you approach a mental threshold and suddenly calm down once you are beyond.

THE NEED FOR A TEACHER

There is an old saying about it being darkest just before the dawn and the approaching of thresholds is sometimes reflective of this. Of course, this means that you actually have to go through the dark bit too and it's a good idea to go into this with the necessary resources. You can do plenty of this practice on your own but at some point, to reach a particular depth and pass the thresholds that hold the general populace, you will need a teacher to guide you.

Usually the practices are self-regulating, meaning that the person will tend to back off approaching the dangerous shadows (that precede some of the most wonderful thresholds) of their own accord until they are ready. Occasionally, I meet kamikazes who thirst for an almost suicidal level of intensity in everything they do and who will take this concept to push the limits of this intensity even further. This doesn't tend to work so well for these people; the balanced approach means that their critical thresholds lie not in the seas of intense sensation, but rather in the currents of gentle, boring exercises that don't seem to be doing much. The guidance of a teacher can help orient us properly in situations such as these.

The teacher is also a useful aid in passing long-term thresholds. Many of the short-term thresholds can be passed by doing a daunting and lengthy single practice, but certain long-term thresholds require ongoing exposure to gentle daily practices that are structured in a particular way to go beyond. There are also cases where a threshold can be passed in either the short or long term, and in yet other cases a combination of both is necessary.

PASSING THRESHOLDS

If you want to learn about which thresholds a particular exercise might help you to pass, my usual recommendation is to maintain that exercise for five to ten minutes non-stop each day, for thirty to sixty uninterrupted days. If you want to get a taste for what a full Daoist practice would be like, you would need to do this with at least one exercise from each category (physical, breathing & mind work) simultaneously: five to ten minutes of physical practice AND five to ten minutes of breathing practice AND five to ten minutes of mind practice, all done every day. Traditionally, 300 days straight is the minimum requirement to find out what the practice does.

There is nothing special or specific about these lengths of time. The recommendation is simply to suggest a minimum exposure to the practice or exercise that should be long enough to provoke the passing of a threshold or two. When the practitioner can experience this for themselves, they will learn at least part of the value of the practice which lets them make a real choice about whether they want to keep going or not.

The problem with being too specific with recommendations is that everyone is a little different in how long it will take. Each individual's history, how well they can maintain attention, what kind of condition their body is in, their willpower and many other factors weave a web that is unique and which makes it more or less impossible to predict how long it might take. I have seen people struggle for more than a year with no sign of anything approaching, then suddenly in a week they pass scores of different thresholds and loads of things fall into place. I have seen slow, steady and predictable progress that ticks along bit by bit, cruising nicely past a threshold in clear fashion. I have seen complete chaos too, watching a student one week be seemingly past a threshold, and the next week back before it again, darting all over the place for many weeks before finally settling beyond. I have also seen all of these situations express in a single individual depending on the practice they were doing or the time of their life.

Even though there are no guarantees about *when* it will work, if you approach practising these exercises with the thresholds in mind you might just find yourself beyond a few in less time than you expect. We have a saying in our school: *if you do it, it works.* The secret ingredient here is the sustaining of effort, both in the short term (don't interrupt your session if you can at all avoid it!) and in the long-term (don't miss any days, even a small effort of five to ten minutes can make a huge difference). I remember one of the critical turning points in my practice where I challenged myself to do thirty minutes of breathing practice every day for 300 days straight. Although on many of these days I only managed five or ten minutes, I only had a single day where I didn't do anything – it was the day I proposed to my wife, and in my excitement, I forgot about it completely. Funnily enough, we both awoke at the same time in the middle of the night and sat bolt upright and simultaneously commented about how I had missed my training for the day. When I looked at the clock, it was already 5:30 am: the next morning already! Despite the bump in the road, I pushed on. As I progressed through the remaining days and continued on afterwards, many changes that I expected to be years or decades away occurred within months. Even more interestingly, many capacities that I had thought were impossible pipe dreams, only reserved for the lucky few, were now my lived reality after a couple of years.

Chapter 2:

Fundamental Practices

....

fundamental
[fuhn-duh-men-tl]

adjective
*   *serving as, or being an essential part of,*
    a foundation or basis; basic; underlying

*   *of, relating to, or affecting the foundation*
    or basis

*   *being an original or primary source.*

noun
*   *a basic principle, rule, law, or the like,*
    that serves as the groundwork of a system;
    essential part.

Building a Strong Foundation

The Da Xuan school has many hundreds, possibly even thousands of exercises. Thankfully, the only ones who have to memorise it all are the guardians of the tradition. The point of having such a huge library of exercises to draw on is to make sure there is something to suit each individual. Of course, helping a student navigate this smorgasbord of exercises is the role of the teacher. Although many of the exercises are optional, every student must practise certain fundamental exercises to build a proper foundation for the other exercises.

This chapter will describe the very first of these foundational exercises so that you may begin practice. For the uninitiated, they will give you a taste of what Daoist practice is all about – if it resonates with you, you may be inspired to seek out a teacher for further exercises. For those who are already on their own path, these exercises can provide insights into missing pieces of the foundation and highlight weak points in your practice. You may have already done similar exercises but give these exercises a go – they might surprise you!

Following the ideas from the first chapter, we will organise our exercises in three categories: Mind, Breathing and Body. The exercises for the mind will build basic concentration so we can do our practice without our thoughts wandering. We will study the tricks of the mind so when we inevitably bump up against resistance, we know what's happening. The exercises for breathing will teach us about the breath's regulating function, and we will find out how to improve our vitality by training the breathing action and the lung capacity. Physically, we will work on basic posture, where we are in space and which direction we are going (starting with the hands) and discovering the hidden tension that glues sections of our body together without us knowing about it.

A problem with the simplicity of the exercises is that we either think we can already do them or, on the flip side, assume that they are not possible because our society does a pretty good job at smothering our basic functions. When we use these exercises to learn about the way we function, we can quickly be confronted by the parts of ourselves that we don't like – these are called *shadows* in Da Xuan. This confrontation is often shocking and takes significant energy to accept and digest properly. We practise so we have the energy to confront these shadows and thereby face our fears and learn more about ourselves.

Try to keep this in mind as you read through the explanations and try the exercises. We will start with the mind and work our way down to the body. Let's begin!

Meditation

We have plenty of meditation practices in Da Xuan and I cannot talk about training the mind without discussing the term a little. It's a hot topic these days and, as a result, the word has been hijacked by popular culture to refer to many different things, which confuses the topic considerably. I regularly hear people say things like, '*insert activity* is my meditation' (where the activity is anything from running to gardening, or from knitting to hiking). While it may be a soothing or relaxing experience, or give you some much needed time to let the mind wander free from the constant attention to everything that is asked of us today, this has little to do with revealing the truth of who we are, nor does it really train us to keep our mind strictly in one place for long periods of time. Having activities like these to absorb ourselves in can produce many wonderful results, but they do not produce the *same* results as specific meditation practices, so cannot act as a substitute for them. When meditation means *everything*—from disconnecting from the hustle and bustle to relaxing to breathing to sitting still and doing nothing—it means nothing at all. We must bring back clarity by being precise with our terms.

In Da Xuan we have two sides to the training of the mind: meditation (called *Shen Dan*) and training the mental qualities (called *Shen Gong*). We say 'who we are' is made up of three parts: who we really are, who we think we are and who we pretend to be. Meditation, as we define it, is a very specific practice that is to do with realising (and later being able to freely access) *who we really are*. It is a process of surrender and putting down control which allows us to return to our source, which is unborn, undying, infinite and completely perfect. It's a deep topic, as you might imagine.

On the other side of the spectrum we have the training of the mind (Shen Gong), which is about practices that build specific mental qualities such as the ability to concentrate on a single point for a long period of time without thinking about other things, and the ability to maintain a general awareness of your surroundings while keeping your precise focus. You can build very strong mental qualities and have made **no** inroads at all into meditation, but it is very difficult to make any kind of progress in meditation without having strong mental qualities. You can see we need both, and you could easily categorise them as Yin and Yang and see again that one is not more important than the other. Practically speaking, we work on the qualities *first*, and then go about doing our meditation once the qualities of our mind are sufficiently developed.

If the whole bit about meditation being related to accessing the infinite part of ourselves has caught your interest, I would highly recommend following a teacher and tradition with a long history of accomplishing such things – it's a risky and dangerous business to be doing it on your own; there are many dead ends and traps that can leave you worse off than when you started. For these reasons and because of the depth of the topic, I will stick to discussing the training of mental qualities, which are not dangerous at all and will prepare you nicely should you want to embark on a meditation practice.

Training the Mind (Shen)

As we just discussed, the Daoist term for working on the qualities of the mind is *Shen Gong*. *Shen* simultaneously refers to the mind and spirit, and *Gong* simply means to work on or train something.

In Shen Gong we are developing capacity to direct, focus, stabilise and relax the mind. You can think of the mind like a torch with an aperture. Firstly, we can point the torch at different things and bring the light of awareness to them (focus). We can also keep the torch pointed at one thing for long periods of time without moving it around (concentration) or open the aperture to have a softer, more diffuse light filling a large space. Whatever the light touches is illuminated in our consciousness (awareness). The aperture of the mind can be opened widely to light the entire space like a lamp or closed tightly to direct our attention to a specific point like a laser.

Think of being in a cinema or reading a message on your phone. Our mind narrows onto what we are doing and we can get so absorbed in this concentrated focus that we lose awareness of what is going on around us. Alternatively, we can open the mind right up to experience everything that is going on at once. Imagine being in a big shopping centre and taking in all the sights and sounds – we become aware of many things going on, it's very busy and we tend to lose our capacity for specific focus. This is the general awareness that is the other side of the coin.

In Da Xuan, the word *mindfulness* has a very specific definition. It means *simultaneously* keeping awareness of the specific (the laser) and the general (the lamp), both internally and externally. To be absorbed in the specific, at the loss of awareness of the general, or to be absorbed in our internal world at the expense of the external world—even if you are doing a great internal practice—is to lose mindfulness. Likewise, to only have general awareness without a capacity to focus on a specific point misses the mark too. Most people are able to access this kind of multi-spectrum awareness that we call mindfulness for a few seconds without practice. But it takes a lot of practice to maintain it for minutes, hours, days or weeks without interruption and, even more to be able to maintain this constantly throughout the dynamic parts of life. To train it, we must train in a way that changes the conscious *and* unconscious parts of the mind, the latter of which is often more responsible for causing us to become distracted or absorbed by a particular sliver of what we perceive.

Two points about training the mind (and practice in general). Firstly, even if you think things are going horribly wrong somehow, you can always use this to learn about how you function (thinking things are going wrong is one of many functions the mind excels at!). Secondly, remember that results don't dictate results, intention dictates results – a baby learns to walk by intending to learn how to walk, not by being excellent at it on the first go (or the millionth go).

GETTING TO KNOW THE MIND

I'll talk more about intention soon, but let's go into more detail on the first point: understanding that a big part of the work on the mind is the simple task of getting to *know* the mind. To begin our practice, we sit down with an exercise and with an intention for the mind to do something specific. When it inevitably *doesn't* do it, we get some very interesting information. First of all, we start to see that we do not have as much control of our minds as we thought, unknown and uncontrollable factors send our attention this way and that, despite our best efforts. If we read into this a little, we might be able to see that *we aren't our mind* – if we were, surely, we could just do what we wanted. The mind is not at all who we are; it's much more like a roommate who talks too much but can also be amazingly helpful.

We want to start to get to know the way the mind operates. It has a little (read: big) bag of tricks that it uses to distract us from the task we set it. When we direct the mind to do something apart from its normal free-for-all of thinking and pretending to be in charge, it puts it in the position of being the servant instead of the king. Like anyone being dethroned, the mind is not, at first, fond of the notion of service and so will begin to use all the tricks it has at its disposal to prevent you from usurping it. If we are steadfast in our resolve to stay with the exercise, slowly the mind will reveal more and more tricks as it tries desperately to stop you. Distracting thoughts, false tiredness, defocused vision, optical and sensory illusions like itches and pain, bombardments of thoughts telling you to stop for any and every conceivable reason and many more things can and probably will happen. When we notice these things happen, as well as bringing our attention back to the task at hand, we can take a moment to appreciate that we just learnt another little trick of the mind and as such we know how our mind operates a little more clearly.

Every time you get to the end of your intended practice time without quitting mid-way through, you have made progress in getting to know your mind. You are making it clear, particularly to the unconscious parts of the mind, that no matter what stunt it pulls you will see the practice through and you are also learning how a big part of the mind functions through trickery and deception (which is *the normal function of the mind*). These tricks can often make you feel as though you are not progressing. The mental qualities tend to seep in sideways; you will feel you are fighting a losing battle against a mind with endless tricks until you pass an invisible threshold and suddenly it doesn't feel like that and you don't even really remember when it changed.

The opponent has transformed into a willing ally and faithful servant (that will still occasionally try to pretend to be in charge when it finds an opportune moment – what a funny thing the mind is!). *When* this happens is different for different people and cannot be easily predicted. It will just happen at some point near or far and how long it takes is not a problem at all. I'll emphasise again: *what makes the practices of the mind work best is simply showing up and doing it as best you can and continuing to do so regardless of the perceived results.*

It is also worth noting that while this kind of practice may *result* in an overall more relaxed mind, the practice itself can sometimes be quite a tiring task. We all know this – everyone has experienced focus and concentration become progressively more difficult when they are exhausted. Practising to keep these elements strictly in one place is draining at the time, but will work over the long term to reduce the general overspend of energy we have in the mind. Once these resources have been freed up, you will feel progressively more energised and relaxed when you aren't doing the practice. It also requires progressively *less* energy to do our practice as the mind becomes more compliant and willing to be of service.

Remember, as we are practising the qualities of the mind (which are very non-tangible/Yang in nature), we do not want to concern ourselves with what the body is doing. The *only* requirement for the body is that it be as comfortable as possible. No particular posture is necessary. Sit upright so you don't crank your neck and then make it as comfortable as you can. If you worry about whether or not your posture is correct then you are working on the body and not the mental qualities.

INTENTION

I want to be extremely clear about this point by repeating it many times: *intention dictates results*. If you begin with the intention to work on the mind and sit down and do your practice for the time you wanted, you have already done the *best possible practice* for that time period – regardless of how distracted you were or if your mind doesn't do the task during the practice. Taking a moment before any practice, mental, physical or otherwise, to make clear what your intention is for that practice is a valuable habit. Start with how long you plan to practise for (or that you will not be following a specific timeframe). You might also have the intention to be particular with corrections, always adjusting as soon as you notice one little problem. Alternatively, you could intend to make no corrections and just enjoy the practice that day, however it comes out. Make clear which quality you are working on. If you are about to begin a Red Ball practice (see below), you could set your intention as 'only concerned with the focus on the shape and not with the body or the breath.' This can become a very quick process taking only a second, but in the beginning, it can be nice to have a formal process where you take three breaths, relax, state your intentions (internally is fine) and then begin practice.

To begin training the mind we will use a simple focus exercise and a couple of thought watching exercises that are more geared towards exploring the content of the mind.

Exercises for the Mind

Try focusing on the red ball for five minutes straight every day. When you are comfortable, increase it to ten minutes, then fifteen, twenty, and later thirty minutes. Once you can focus on the red ball for thirty minutes, change to the second drill for one month, then the third drill for one month.

1. The Red Ball

Sit comfortably and put a simple geometric shape (circle, square, triangle) of a single flat colour at eye level a metre or two in front of you. A red circle is traditional but any shape and dark colour will do. Stare at the shape without doing anything else, trying only to see the shape. Ignore all else that is going on either internally or externally.

2. Thought Watching

Sit or lie comfortably. Simply watch your own thoughts as they appear and disappear in your mind. Keep the sense of distance from the thoughts, in the same way that you had distance between yourself and the red ball in the exercise above. You don't need to do anything here except watch the thoughts as they come and go.

3. Acceptance – The Yes Method

Sit or lie comfortably. Watch your thoughts as they pass through your mind, as per the exercise above. Every time a thought appears, meet it with an attitude of 'Yes', acknowledging the reality that the thought has appeared, regardless of what the thought is about. It helps to keep a gentle smile on your face as you do this! Happily, meet the reality of thoughts appearing in your mind, both good and bad. I like to call this exercise 'Daoist Tinder' – whatever appears, just swipe right!

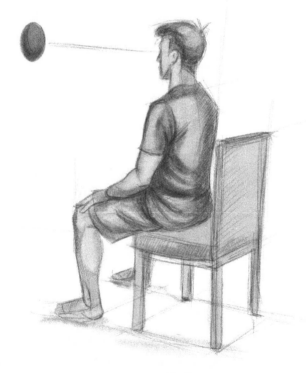

put the red circle (or other simple shape) at eye level and stare directly at it

Figure 3 — Red ball setup

Training the Breath and Circulation (Qi)

The next section covers exercises which relate to training the vital energy or circulation. There are a few terms here that are used in specific ways in Da Xuan. When our intention is to work on the energy (written *Qi,* pronounced *'Chee'*) while seated and without moving, we call it *Nèi Dān* – *Nei* literally means 'internal' and *Dan* refers to the alchemical process. When we use movements, but the intention is directed towards feeling the energy rather than the motion or posture, we call it either *Nei Gong* or *Qi Gong* – the terms are interchangeable. *Nei* meaning 'internal', *Qi* referring to the energy or breath as I'll discuss further below, and *Gōng,* used throughout, meaning to train or work on.

Whether we are in motion or not, the work on the energy revolves primarily around having the intention on breathing, feeling sensations of energy and circulation, and finally learning to direct those sensations throughout the body and later beyond the bodily limits. The breath regulates emotions and helps us to digest our problems and confrontations by creating energy for the process; keeping this energy circulating makes sure anything stuck in our system gets moving again.

FUEL

We have three ways of creating new energy – food, drink (aka our diet), and breath. Other processes may free up energy that was previously bound in stasis, but this is not actually generating new energy, just releasing what was already there but stuck. To generate new energy is a process requiring fuel – something that is 'not us' is taken in and transformed into energy for us. This is a magical process that is happening right beneath our noses as we eat, drink and breathe!

Eating and drinking can only generate so much energy, as it requires us to use energy to assimilate it through the digestive processes. We can increase the net output by eating a balanced diet, but we must consider that with all the clashing advice on the topic these days, we can end up using tremendous energy overthinking and overanalysing. At some point, this will work against the overall goal of generating more energy. If you want to diet, you will need to use a method that doesn't bother you emotionally/socially and doesn't need you to think about it too much. In this sense simple is better. The Daoist guide for diet is pretty straightforward: eat fresh meat and vegetables as close to when they were harvested as possible, keep a good but simple variety, prepare it yourself whenever possible, avoid pre-chopped and pre-prepared meals, *chew and taste* your food, and try not to do anything else while you are eating so you can focus on the food and its taste. Other dietary options depend on the person. I will generally only recommend a specific diet where the benefit of following the diet will outweigh the mental and emotional stress generated by the restrictions.

BECOMING AWARE OF THE BREATH

The breath on the other hand has lots of untapped potential. Like food, the breath must be assimilated. The process of exchange takes something that is not us and transforms it into us and, in return, we take something that *is* us and transform it into not us, expelling it. The assimilation of the breath can be improved by simply feeling the exchange more precisely. The average breath taken by a regular city dweller is about 0.5L. This can easily be increased by two to **ten** (!!!) fold *as soon as you pay conscious attention to your breathing*. It's in our best interest to do this as often as possible. We can also (with practice) dramatically increase our lung capacity and improve how effectively the breath is assimilated, so we can both take more in and make better use of that taken in. In my own experience, I have already taken this far beyond what I imagined was possible. This change has been so vivid that I'm no longer sure of the upper limits of possibilities, especially if it keeps growing as it has since the beginning. Doing this without any other energy expenditure is the best way to increase energy reserves.

Here we run into a bit of a conundrum. As we saw earlier, having to concentrate hard to keep the awareness focused solely on the breath *uses* energy and so is not ideal. To buffer for this, we will make use of techniques that have minimal energetic cost to gently keep the awareness on the breath without turning it into a focus exercise (which would just be repeating the work on the mental qualities rather than working on the breath).

If the mind wanders away from the breath it also uses energy generating thoughts – we are no longer aiding the exchange by feeling the breath and we have lost our directing capacity. Ideally, we can relax the mind and feel the breath without any particular technique or force required.

FEELING THE ENERGY

The exchange of the breath is a process that extends—and can be felt—beyond the lungs. The Chinese word for this whole process is 'Qi', but this word comes with so much baggage these days that it's difficult to use without misunderstanding. Rather than any fantasies about magical energy, we can just keep it simple: feeling the circulation! If we can tap into this extended feeling, we can increase our capacity for assimilation of the breath energy even more. On a physical level, the oxygen transfer doesn't just stop in the lungs. From the lungs it is transferred to the heart and attached to the blood and then diffused through every cell of the body where it exchanges the fresh oxygen for waste products which are then transported out of the body. There is also a small amount of air being absorbed by the skin at any given point. The energetic sensations of this 'breath-exchange' can be felt with increasing clarity with practice. The more clearly we can feel it, the better our breath is assimilated, expanding the possibilities for working with the energy.

In the beginning, it is incredibly difficult to feel at all and we must therefore reduce the noise coming from movements of the body by either not moving at all (*Nei Dan*) or moving very slowly and simply (nei gong/qi gong). We will start by focusing our attention towards the places in the body that are easiest to feel – primarily the obvious pathway of the breath through the throat and lungs, and the hands (training the hands in this manner is part of a qi gong practice not within the scope of this book to discuss, but important enough to warrant a quick mention).

Our attention should be on the sensations of breath or energy to keep us focused on training this aspect of the trinity. Beginners will often fall out of the internal/energetic training and into external/physical training where the intention has returned to the body, motion, posture, relaxation, and so on. This is a normal stage to pass through. You need only be clear about when you *intend* to train externally or internally, and when you are training internally, make a genuine effort to stay in the feeling even though it will not always transpire that way. Remember, intention dictates results, and we can only get better by trying with clear intentions.

For this training we can use multiple differing but complementary paths: simple breathing practices for improving basic lung capacity and the action of breathing; qi gong or static postures to improve the capacity to feel and circulate, and/or the internal alchemy practices (Nei Dan) to heat the centre and work on the small and big orbits. Generally, the simple practices of the breath are the best place to start, in Da Xuan the exercises that introduce Nei Dan are part of a sub-syllabus called *Primordial Breathing*.

Exercises for the Breath

Try doing the first exercise every day for a month, then do the second exercise every day of the following month, and then the third exercise every day of the third month. Return to the first exercise in the fourth month and see how it has changed.

1.   Conscious Breathing

Sit in any comfortable position with the torso upright, straight and relaxed. Lay the hands in the lap or over the navel. Breathe in and think 'breathing in'. Breathe out and think 'breathing out'. Don't do anything else. Do not interfere with the breath or push any kind of idea about how you should be breathing. Just let it go however it's going without trying to improve it. Stay for between ten and thirty minutes.

2.   Abdominal Breathing

Lie face up on the ground with the arms by the side, the feet planted flat on the ground, the knees bent and pointing directly upwards. Place a small weight (2–5kg – a thick book works well) on your navel. Breathe in so that the belly expands without the spine coming off the ground at all, lifting the weight as high as you can towards the ceiling and taking in as much air as you can. Relax completely to let the weight go down and push the breath out for you. Try to make the exhale last twice as long as the inhale. Continue for ten to thirty minutes straight.

breathe in, press the weight up

breathe out, let the weight sink down

Figure 4 — Lying abdominal breathing

3. Static Posture Internal Training

Stand with your feet shoulder width apart, knees soft, your toes pointing straight ahead, your back straight as if stretched gently between head and tailbone, your arms hanging relaxed by your side, your chin gently tucked, your crown lifted upwards and your eyes looking neither up nor down. Breathe in and put all your attention towards feeling the crown of your head, as if you wanted to push it high into the sky (but don't move!). Breathe out and put all your attention towards feeling the soles of the feet, as if you wanted to push them deep into the ground. Notice any feelings that move towards the head or feet. Repeat this cycle for ten to thirty minutes straight.

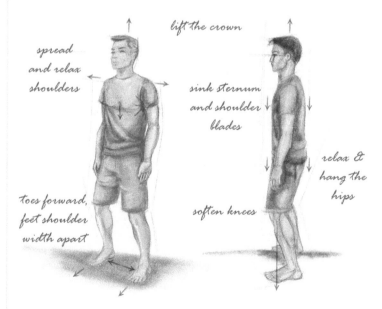

lift the crown

spread and relax shoulders

sink sternum and shoulder blades

relax & hang the hips

toes forward, feet shoulder width apart

soften knees

Figure 5 — Static postures

Training the Physical Body (Jing)

The work on the body (called *Wài Gōng — Wai* simply means external) is the easiest to work with because it is completely tangible and progress is obvious. In Da Xuan we have some basic qualities we need to acquire and then we can be free to pursue the physical activities that we are most drawn to. For people outside the tradition, the simple exercises and basic qualities we practise here are really useful just to keep us feeling good throughout life and in many other physical endeavours.

SIMPLICITY

We spend the first few years developing the general physical qualities using simple exercises.

This kind of physical training often appears boring. Especially in the beginning, the exercises seem dull and like they don't do much. They don't offer any possibility of something you can present to others. The improvements that come are obvious to the practitioner but not at all something that you can video or photo and proudly send to friends. As you gain experience and begin to notice the subtle changes it becomes easier to motivate yourself. Sooner or later you really *feel* what the exercises do for you, how wonderful they are despite their plain outward appearance, and you become more and more motivated to practise. There is also a kind of deep satisfaction in doing something that offers no value for status — you do it for its own sake, regardless of the opinion of others.

The basic qualities we want to train are as follows:

GROUNDING

Physical, mechanical grounding means we can hold our position and not be moved by someone trying to push or pull against us. We have simple partner drills for this and also plenty of static postures that allow us to practise grounding solo.

STRUCTURE AND STRENGTH

The building of the structure is split into two elements: the uncoupling of certain structures which are inappropriately bound, for example uncoupling hip movement from shoulder movement by freeing the waist; and the strengthening of the weak connections that are not working properly, such as the connection from the back to the arms via the insertion of latissimus dorsi in the armpits.

Developing the structure like this will make sure that our state is not one of fighting ourselves or gravity. This leaves our available strength to be used for the task at hand. In other words, our strength comes from our structure. Because our training specifically targets the weakest points in the body, we are able to significantly reduce the contrast between weak and strong links. By training like this, we unite our body into one unit that does not move against itself. We can see from this that strength and structure go hand in hand. More on structure and tension later.

COORDINATION AND RELAXATION

General coordination is something that comes when the body can easily be felt in space and when both the mind and body are sufficiently relaxed. Learning a new motion that is not beyond your current physical capacity is a good practice and a good test to see how relaxed you are, and how well your mind is connected to your body. The more relaxed you are, the easier it will be to pick up the new motion. Ideally it should only take a few attempts.

TRAINING THE PHYSICAL QUALITIES

I have included a few of the most important of the exercises we use below, but we have many more than this and also plenty of partner drills that can greatly aid in the embodiment of qualities. In Da Xuan, after we have the foundation established, we begin more specific work using nei gong and internal martial arts such as *Tai Ji, Xing Yi, or Bagua*. If you've done some work on the basics and are interested in these more complex practices, direct guidance from a teacher will be necessary.

Physical Exercises

Split your physical training time up into five-minute intervals. For example, if you have fifteen minutes to work, set your timer so a bell rings at five minutes and ten minutes before the final bell sounds at fifteen minutes. Populate each interval with any of the five exercises from the list below. Practise each exercise for the full five minutes without ceasing or interrupting your practice, and when the bell rings, do your best to transition smoothly into the next exercise without interruption. Every thirty days rotate one or two exercises out and replace them with new ones or exercises you haven't done in a while.

Once you are comfortable with all the exercises like this, pick one of the exercises and challenge yourself to go non-stop for ten, fifteen or even thirty minutes in that single exercise. Your entire physical session will now only be one exercise. Continue practising only this single extended exercise for at least two weeks before rotating in a new exercise to repeat the process above.

Once you have done this with all the exercises, return to the first arrangement of five-minute intervals with multiple exercises and see what has changed as the result of your efforts.

1. Basic Directions

Stand with your feet shoulder width apart, knees soft, your toes pointing straight ahead, your back straight as if stretched gently between head and tailbone, your chin gently tucked, your crown lifted upwards and your eyes looking neither up nor down. Have the hands flat and extended out in front of you as if they were resting on a table. The elbows should be relaxed but not too bent. Move the hands up as high as you can and then as low as you can without going either left or right, and without going forward or backwards. The palms should stay parallel to the ground the whole time and fingers pointing forwards. Practice moving the hands this way slowly for five minutes straight.

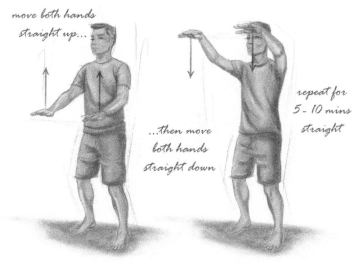

move both hands straight up...

...then move both hands straight down

repeat for 5 - 10 mins straight

Figure 6 — Up down exercise

Once you are familiar with the up-down direction, try the left-right direction. Set up in the same posture only this time the palms are facing each other. Move the hands as far away from the centre as you can (left palm travelling left, right to the right) without going up or down, and without going forward or backward. The palms should stay facing each other and the fingers pointing forward the entire time. Practice moving the hands this way slowly for five minutes straight.

keep closing until they are about chest width apart

move the palms hooryiontally towards each other, closing

from there move the palms apart again, opening

repeat for 5-10 mins straight

Figure 7 — Left right exercise

The last direction is forward-backward. Using the same posture again, let the hands hang by the sides with the palms facing backward, and the fingers pointing straight down to the ground. Move the palms as far forward and backward as you can without them going left or right, and without moving them up or down.

move the palms from front to back

don't let the palms change height

repeat for 5 - 10 mins straight

then move palms from back to front

Figure 8 — Forward back exercise

2. Uncoupling the Waist

Stand with your feet shoulder-width apart, knees soft, your toes pointing straight ahead, your back straight as if stretched gently between head and tailbone, your chin gently tucked, your crown lifted upwards and your eyes looking neither up nor down. Have the arms hanging heavy and relaxed by your side. Without the hips moving at all turn the chest, rotating from left to right. Let the arms dangle and swing freely. In the beginning you will need to use tension to hold the hips in place to stop them being dragged around by the chest. As you improve you will be able to relax the hips more while still keeping them from moving.

turn the chest to the right letting the arms relax and swing

bounce off the left and go to the right again

bounce off the right and let the momentum carry you to the left

repeat for 5 - 10 mins straight

Figure 9 — Uncoupling the waist

Figure 10 (facing page) — Flattening the back into the ground

3. Flattening the Back into the Ground

Lie face up on the ground with the arms by the side, the feet planted flat on the ground, the knees bent and pointing directly upwards. Keep your whole spine glued to the ground. Take your time to relax a little. Without letting the spine come away from the ground, lift one foot so it is hovering just above the ground, then extend the leg hovering the foot along the ground the whole way, before finally putting the whole leg on the ground and relaxing it. Do the same with the other leg so you end up lying flat. Keep the legs and hips as relaxed as you possibly can during the whole process. In the beginning a significant effort will be needed in the abdominals to keep the spine glued to the ground. As you improve, tension will reduce and you will be able to keep the spine glued with less effort. Your intention is to move through the positions and rest in each position as relaxed as possible, but always with the spine glued to the ground.

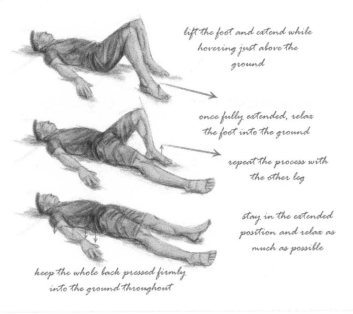

lift the foot and extend while hovering just above the ground

once fully extended, relax the foot into the ground

repeat the process with the other leg

stay in the extended position and relax as much as possible

keep the whole back pressed firmly into the ground throughout

Overview

What we are establishing in a general sense can be simply summarised like so:

Mind – Relaxed to free energy from unnecessary thinking, available to be focused when needed.

Breath – Deeper breathing and a clear feeling of circulation to generate more energy and be more relaxed. More energy available means better digestion of emotions and allows us to face the challenges of life completely.

Body – Strong, aligned structure (no weak links) to allow us to move with no unnecessary tension, motion to keep everything circulating fluidly and not let stagnation build or rebuild. General physical capacity so we can participate in life properly. Grounding to prevent us getting lost in fantasy from too much energetic/mental/spiritual training.

There are two big ideas that I would like to make explicit now:

1. If we know how we function more clearly, we have more information about ourselves and can therefore make better choices in life.

2. We cannot do away with the challenges of life but we can increase our energy so we can meet them with vitality.

Chapter 3:

Orienting Ideas, Concepts
& Other Frameworks

....

orientation
[awr-ee-uh n-tey-shuh n, -en-, ohr-]

noun

- *an introduction, as to guide one in adjusting to new surroundings, employment, activity, or the like*

- *Psychology, Psychiatry: the ability to locate oneself in one's environment with reference to time, place, and people*

- *one's position in relation to true north, to points on the compass, or to a specific place or object*

- *the ascertainment of one's true position, as in a novel situation, with respect to attitudes, judgments, etc.*

Ideas Aren't Reality

Unlike the previous chapters, this one is more confined to general ideas that I have developed over a long time with lots of research and trial and error in my life. Some of the ideas are explicitly from the Da Xuan tradition, some not so explicitly but (it seems to me) they are heavily implied. Some of them I have not found in the tradition – maybe they are in there and I just don't know about them yet; at the time of writing I haven't been exposed to every teaching in the tradition.

These ideas frame my practice and help me to make discoveries and grow, but I need to warn: *any* idea or thought, any framework, any model, is **not** reality. If all our attention is caught up in our virtual ideas *about* the world, we will miss what is actually happening *in* the world. The conceptual frameworks can help to orient us in reality but are not replacements *for* reality. A compass can point north, but looking at a compass and believing it is pointing north is not a replacement for following it and seeing for yourself if it takes you north, nor can it tell you anything about what it's like to be in the north. You can even follow a compass while completely disbelieving it is taking you north and still arrive in the north, as long as you take the steps in the direction indicated. The little arrow in your hand is a virtual representation of that direction but is not the direction itself.

As we can see, just because something is virtual or imagined does not mean it has no practical use. While the virtual arrow is not itself north, it can help us to get to north. Our capacity to imagine and idealise is what sets us apart from the animal kingdom. It is unfortunate that the popularity of scientific rationalism has given us the perception that things that are imagined, and therefore irrational, are not worthwhile (while we ironically indulge the hell out of our own virtual constructions). To add to this problem, many new-age spiritual movements have a huge grudge against the ego, whose very function is to create these virtual boundaries and separate the unity of life into something more organised. When this function is diminished, we lose our capacity for clear judgement and decision making that comes from analysis. Like geographic borders which are abstract but still work to contain entire countries and cultures, these boundaries in the mental world are illusions that nevertheless have incredible utility.

We just have to be careful not to corrupt the usage and mistake utility for reality. Searching for an experience of the unity of life is a noble goal for sure, but without the possibility of using the ego to create these virtual containers and separate things into this and that, we may end up not much better off than a newborn. Newborn babies live in the unity of life but can't function in the world in a useful way because they cannot differentiate between themselves and others, between this and that.

I like the word *framework* because it gives us an impression of this function of division and separation: to frame our reality. The function of having ideas is to help us make sense of what we are seeing, or to highlight where we could be doing something in a different way so as not to go against ourselves so much. As with any foray into the world of ideas, concepts, imagination, and spirituality (very Yang in nature), we must always balance ourselves by confronting our ideas with what is actually happening and manifested (Yin). One is not more important than the other. We want the practicality of being able to orient ourselves by making clear distinctions and boundaries using our virtual ideas, AND we want to always remember that these boundaries and the ideas and knowledge that construct them are virtual – the singular reality of life is only ever what is happening *right now* and it's very easy to miss right now when we are too caught up in the virtual realm of ideas.

At some point we need to let go of our tight grip on these concepts and relax about it all. To stick too firmly to any of these single ideas is to miss the main point about balance. They are guides but not absolute truths – more like rules of thumb or heuristics. They are very useful if you apply them to your life and invest in practising this application, but quite noxious if you keep them to throw at people who disagree with you without actually confronting or changing any of your habits and patterns of behaviour. It is always better to *do silently* than it is to *talk* without doing.

Speaking of doing silently, while many of these ideas can have great use at the appropriate time, they can also become toxic if we indulge too much in their pursuit. Even if you are striking a good balance by making positive changes, it is necessary to put down these ideas regularly, stop thinking about them, stop considering them, stop looking for patterns, and stop analysing. Just let life be and be with your loved ones without considering patterns and cultivation and anything else mentioned in this book or anywhere else for that matter. Putting them down for a time will make you less neurotic about your practice and let you engage in it in a pleasant way. It will give your unconscious a period of much needed relaxation to digest everything you've discovered and confronted. This does not mean you stop doing your daily exercises, it just means that you *also* take time to live your life and engage with those around you completely.

I have struggled, and still struggle, coming to terms with this myself and finding balance is an ongoing effort. To help bring about some more clarity on this difficult subject, I'd like to share some more tales about these struggles ...

ADDICTION TO INFORMATION

I am by nature an academic person. I was a straight 'A' student in school and finished with a university entrance rank of over 90 percent without too much effort on my part. I have a good capacity to see and hear something and then near-instantly begin to tear it apart mentally and create an intellectual concept of how it works. As I mentioned above, our current society values rational and intellectual knowledge very highly, so this capacity of mine has served me very well for most of my life.

However, at some point I became addicted to knowing the information, especially knowledge of the underlying concepts – the why and how at the root. My need to understand intellectually resulted in an addiction to collecting information (including proofs and concepts and systems) *about* something instead of having a direct experience of the same thing – even when the option to have direct experience was available. As I have already alluded to, it can be a great tool if used correctly, though at some point I created a mental perversion out of this tool.

There was something of a laziness involved in this process, too – my mind is faster at building conceptual frameworks than my physical body is at actually manifesting these same concepts so it was easier and faster for me to *understand* rather than *do*.

Abstraction is essentially fantasy – when I build a concept in my mind it is entirely imaginary until it is lived. The problem that my practice exposed is that I was abstracting everything, but not using the abstraction to do anything (except perhaps argue with people who disagreed with it). At some point, I had stopped using the abstracting as a tool to help me live in the wonder of the world and instead was living in my constructed fantasy. I had built myself a preconceived idea about how I was, how other people were and how the world was and, in the process, had completely divorced myself from what was actually going on. Because this abstraction occurred so quickly, it happened without my noticing it. Even entirely new events were quickly torn apart, analysed and categorised to fit into my pre-existing boxes. Never mind experience – what mattered was that I 'knew'.

This fast and impatient knowing created a kind of arrogance. I knew – and the often-not-so-subtle implication was that I knew it better than whomever I was talking to. Sub-consciously I looked down upon people who did not know, either with a fake sympathy – 'oh those poor people who don't know'; or a kind of looking down on the 'stupid person who did not understand – and never would'.

This was all happening internally and sub-consciously of course. I wasn't actively choosing to behave like such a giant ass (most of the time). I also suspect that the majority of it was camouflaged from others, manifesting to the outside world by subtle expression visible only to the very keen-eyed.

There have been many funny periods for me as I began looking into this addiction. Even when I started to understand that knowing information is not the same as *knowledge* that resulted from direct experience, the compulsion that wanted to know about this (which created the whole addiction in the first place) immediately kicked in and began building a new intellectual box to accommodate this 'knowing-that-knowing-is-not-*knowing*'. Quickly I was patting myself on the back for being so clever as to have worked it out. It took several experiences of a deep confrontation with myself to actually begin to deconstruct the created framework without replacing it with a new, more advanced version. There was no way to change or upgrade what I knew about the topic without feeding the addiction. To live the knowledge directly, to have *knowledge,* I had to give up believing in the knowledge *about* the topic.

Herein lies the difference between 'knowledge' and *knowledge.* The former is entirely theoretical, but the latter is a visceral experience that, when lived, removes the need for the belief in (or even the existence of) the former. It's not that the theoretical knowledge won't still appear as thoughts and ideas, it's just that it becomes clear that it isn't the reality and we are no longer bound by it.

CONFRONTATION

This experience of confronting my addiction to 'knowing' was quite horrifying. I felt this very ugly part of myself. I was faced with memories of endless reading of internet posts and arguing with strangers online and countless moments of explaining and lecturing like an expert on topics that I had only just been exposed to myself. It was all an intellectual peacock dance – showing the world (mostly myself) how smart I was. I was reminded of the countless times my father had said 'you're trying to be smart but you're only halfway there' as he roused on me for being a 'technically-correct-ass-hat' (my words, not his).

There was a surge of intense emotions that came with this confrontation. I felt that I had disturbed something that was buried very deep. Deep sadness, anger, and wild cackling at the absolute hilarity of it all came bubbling to the surface at random times (sometimes simultaneously), mostly during my practice. I had a number of weeks in a row where I felt quite flat due to the emotional turmoil happening just beneath the surface. There's certainly more to come as well. I am not done peering into this mirror of penance.

To move forward required a birth of innocence in my life and my practice. I had to let go of my attempt at being an expert; to stop trying to out-smart, out-know or 'hack' my practice and instead start to live it. Innocence does not have expectation of results. I feel more and more like a child learning to crawl without expecting to know how to run or knowing if walking is a thing that I will someday be able to do.

These burdens of knowing have been heavy things to carry around. There were so many things that I had to take care of when I 'knew' about something – endless contemplation of endless topics and the constant internal creation of scenarios with imaginary adversaries to whom I would explain my perceived cleverness and a subtle-but-constant threat of humiliation for not knowing enough (that is, not knowing everything ever).

There is a seed of doubt that I feel I have planted in myself – and it grows: 'how much do I really know about myself, my practice and the world?' The more I learn, the more apparent it is how little I know. Every time I have made some significant progress, I have looked back at the previous incarnation of myself – 'That guy ... haha, he thought he knew everything. *You knew nothing Jon Snow!*' Maybe the current me also doesn't really know much at all? Huzzah! This doubt is experienced not as anxiety but rather as a somewhat curious and ever unfolding mystery that I am caught up in.

Being at peace with not knowing where a particular practice leads gave me patience and ease of mind, an enjoyment of where I am right now rather than constantly yearning for the future, even (especially) in the demanding or difficult practices. In an ironic twist, by trying to fulfil my fantasy of practising cleverly with a full understanding of what each practice did before doing it, I was actually blocking many practices from working effectively.

I still have my history of remembered experience to draw on – my true and unique knowledge that has made me who I am today. The difference is that the fantasy that was twisting the details and exaggerating (or downplaying) things is loosening its grip and allowing clarity to grow in its place. Often, this is clarity about what I do *not* actually know. This is giving me a much clearer sense of who I am, rather than allowing me to dwell in who I pretend to be.

Grounding

Enough about me. Let's look at an example of how we can deceive ourselves into confusing an idea with reality using the topic of grounding. If we read about grounding, what it means, how to do it and so on, we might end up with the idea that we are grounded because we have a lot of information about the topic and have thought about it endlessly. Instead of simply believing that idea, we could confront that idea with reality: can we hold our ground *literally* by standing on one spot for a long time and stay relaxed? What if we make the situation less than ideal, and get someone to actively try and push us or pull us over, can we still hold our ground and not be made to take a step? We could make it even harder and have the person cheat in any way they like to try and move us and see if we can hold our ground despite the circumstances being completely against us. Are we still able to keep our ground then?

If the answer to any of these situations is that we cannot hold our ground, that we have to take a step from our position, escape our discomforts or collapse our comfortable structure, then we might see a discrepancy between what we think we are doing and the reality of what we are actually doing. It's not a problem, just a sign that we need to do more grounding practices and confront reality more regularly. The structure of the body is Yin, it is slow and needs time to change. But if we have invested our entire being into believing our *idea* of being grounded, and then that idea meets reality and is found to be completely incorrect, we might be in for a bit of a shock – more so if our fundamental identity is associated with the thoughts that have just been disproven. If we regularly confront our ideas with less-than-*ideal* realities, and they still work as we thought, or we can see we are improving, then we have a real cause to relax both consciously and unconsciously.

This can easily be witnessed in the martial arts communities. Many people only train in the ideal – a cooperative partner, a perfect execution of technique, no intention for violence or cheating and so on. Their techniques might be well-practised, but they will never be able to unconsciously relax with full confidence unless they have been thoroughly and regularly tested in the messiness of a real conflict.

We see the same issues in spiritual communities. People may practise hours of meditation each day for years straight in an ideal situation, but as soon as you bring in some chaos – let's say a loud construction site right next door to their favourite meditation spot, or an annoying and cruel person, the composure falls apart. I was fortunate enough to have such a loud construction site right next to the room where I did a lot of my training. For two years straight, for eight to ten hours a day, six days a week, I had heavy machinery, jackhammers, metal saws and all sorts of other interruptions happening constantly. I had no choice but to practise and the bad situation allowed me to see if I could maintain my qualities amongst the chaos. I can now *rest* in the idea that I can practise in any situation and not be haunted by an unconscious 'but what if ...'. My idea is grounded in the reality of my having tested it for real.

Uniting Through the Centre

To be grounded is also to be centred. If you look up the antonyms of *ideal* in the dictionary, you will find words like *flawed, imperfect, material, practical, pragmatic.* We have the ideal of being well-grounded (the idea of being able to stay in our position no matter what) that we work towards, and the pragmatic reality of our grounding at any point in time (can we actually hold our position even when things get less than ideal?). To be well-grounded can also mean that the ideal has been confronted by the pragmatic, and *both* have been tended to and linked together, which centres us between these opposites. Our *idea* of what we can do (or what we want to do), and what we actually *can* do, are in harmonious union. Practitioners of Da Xuan do lots of work on the refining of the centre to achieve this union of opposites; you might say the entire tradition revolves around this. Centred is a term that is used in many schools of practice, particularly in martial arts and dance. In my experience, most of the time it is taught in an incredibly vague way with instructions like, 'Try to be more centred'. Some people might get it, most people don't. I was in the camp of nod and smile and hope they don't notice that you have no idea what they mean when I heard such cues. I suspect I am not the only one who has experienced this, so a bit more clarity on what exactly it means to be 'centred' is in order.

To understand the centre, it is necessary to go back to our broader picture of the opposites, Yin and Yang. Our relative experience of the world is governed by opposing forces. The ebb and flow of opposites are the very movement of life itself. It is impossible for one extreme to exist without the other and so in any given element a seed or potential for its opposite exists. This concept is most famously realised by the symbol of the *tàijítú*, more colloquially known in English as the 'Yin and Yang' symbol.

Figure 11 — Yin Yang symbol

Here we see the opposites represented by the colours black (on the right and bottom – Yin) and white (on the left and top – Yang). The curves of the symbol give the impression of movement and mixing, and the whole thing encompassed within a circle shows the cyclical nature of the opposites. Yin Yang theory is an incredibly deep study on its own and I do not want to get too deeply into it here. What is relevant to our discussion, and what is not made apparent by the symbol is the centre – the point around and the space through which the opposites turn. This centre could be conceived of as a point right in the middle of the symbol in-between Yin and Yang, or it could be conceived of as the circle that encapsulates both and which gives the impression of the mixing of Yin and Yang.

We get into tricky linguistic territory here but bear with me. The centre I'm talking about here isn't the opposite of the outside, it's the centre *of* opposites and in this sense is not inside or outside, nor is it polarised or unpolarised. It is neither Yin nor Yang and at the same time it includes both Yin and Yang. Another way I like to phrase it is that it is in-between the opposites. It has a spacious, non-fixed quality about it — a charge of potential as if, at any moment, it could easily go towards either of the opposites, a mix of both, or stay between. It has complete access to either of the opposites without being bound by them and so in a certain sense it fully contains both of the opposites. It is a position of open potential and of the ever-changing manifestation of that potential.

The problem with this explanation is that while it might be a nice idea, ideas don't help anyone unless they can become manifest in reality; they must be *lived*. To take this idea as a belief or concept to hold onto in your mind is to do the very thing that every good spiritual tradition warns against. To make it appear in reality, we need something to do — actually engaging in a practice to bring the idea to life.

In the tradition of Da Xuan, we explore this on the physical level first. The physical is much more tangible and obvious than the emotional or mental realms and so it's much easier to confront the reality of it without being tricked by the mind (whose dualistic nature is *not at all fond* of the paradox of the centre).

CENTRING POSTURE

Let's use this concept to look at our posture, and we will start at our feet. It's useful to gauge the physical limits of the opposites so we have a working point to find that which is in-between those opposites. We can have the feet internally or externally rotated, the weight forward on the toes or back on the heels, pronation (collapsing inwards) or supination (rolling outwards) of the ankle, and we can have the feet close together or wide apart. The in-betweens are, respectively: feet parallel with toes pointing forward (between internal and external rotation), the weight in the middle of the foot (between forward and backwards, and between pronated and supinated) and the feet shoulder-width apart (between too close together and too far apart). Our knees want to be on top of the feet and pointing in the same direction as the toes (related to the pronation and supination of the ankle), and between being too straight and too bent. Our hips must hang relaxed, tilted neither to the posterior nor anterior. The glutes and lower abdominals must be relaxed so the effort descends into the centre of the body closer to the bone (it's not quite right but the function of the psoas muscle in Western anatomy is a decent comparison). Our torsos are straight, the spine is neither in flexion, extension, lateral flexion or rotation at any point. The arms are hanging by the side, the shoulders are between protraction and retraction. The neck is neither too far forward (poke neck/upper crossed syndrome) nor too far back (military posture), the head is lifted and the chin gently tucked with the vision straight ahead (between up and down, between left and right, between both directions of tilt) to balance the hanging hips and create space between each of the vertebrae.

What I've described above is hardly rocket science and most physiotherapists will talk about this kind of posture in some way or another. But we can't just go to a couple of physio appointments and assume all is sorted because we know about it. We need to practise regularly to pass the threshold that allows us to understand and embody it, then we can use this understanding of being in-between to refine it even further. Most people when asked to take such a posture will not be able to take it without torqueing and tensing just about every muscle in their body. A good therapist can possibly massage some of this tension out, but it will return in a day or two. Outside intervention is not sufficient, we must train *ourselves* to be centred without all the excessive tension.

Tension is the opposite of relaxation and so winding ourselves up with heavy tension to achieve this ideal posture is counterproductive to our task of centring, as is going completely slack and relaxed which will collapse the posture. If we recall our idea of spaciousness at the centre, we can use this to direct our position. The setup is a way of arranging the body so there is a feeling of space in each joint — room for things to circulate. To encourage this, we need to find a way to be neither overly tensed nor overly relaxed. In other words, we need to be as open in the joints as possible while simultaneously being as relaxed as possible. If you try with your hand you can get the feeling of it pretty easily: open the hand as wide as you can, and you see it invites a lot of tension into the hand. Relax it as much as possible (just go floppy!) and you see the hand's structure collapses and the fingers roll closed. Try instead opening the hand and separating the fingers as much as you can while simultaneously being as relaxed as you can. If you get it dialled well, you can sometimes find that the hand starts to vibrate or shudder.

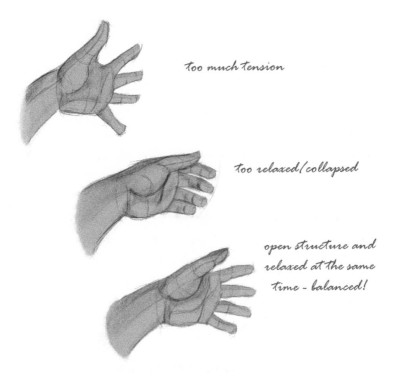

too much tension

too relaxed / collapsed

*open structure and
relaxed at the same
time - balanced!*

Figure 12 — Three hand positions

This vibration is a very typical response when nearing any of the in-betweens mentioned. You can think of it as a confusion of sorts as the body leaves habitual fixation on a particular opposite and starts shifting from one opposite to the other in very quick succession. As you get to a more refined centre position, this vibration will be experienced less on the surface but more deeply in the body, closer to the centre. It eventually creates a paradoxical relaxed tension. The body has structure (tension keeping its shape strongly) but is deeply relaxed and effortless. This conjoining of the opposites is one of the main signs that you are truly in the centre and not just hanging out in an opposite nearby to it.

Unfortunately, there is no quick fix to becoming suddenly perfectly centred. What you can do today though is *orient* yourself towards becoming more centred and refining your lived experience of this, particularly in the physical body. To begin, just take ten minutes a day and practise setting yourself up in the most centred posture you can, then stay there. You might have also noticed that most of the physical exercises make use of centring to set them up. Remember that to be in-between tense and relaxed means that on any given day your most centred posture for that day will be different to what it was on another day, depending on what your hidden tension and stress is doing on that day. In fact, the best current expression of the centre will change as you practice. Of course, we move towards an ideal, but if we don't *also* acknowledge the tensions of the given day, we become oriented towards the extremes and away from the centre. The orientation in this sense has a bigger effect on long term outcomes than worrying about whether the current expression is 'good' or not.

We must also know that it's not useful to only hang out in the centre. The potential of going into one of the opposites can and should manifest at times, we just don't want to get stuck there like our skipping record. We can't truly know that we are in the centre if we aren't intimate with the limits of the extremes, but we do want to have the centre as a home base of sorts that we regularly return to and recuperate. To understand the centre as precisely as possible, we must explore the limits of *both* extremes. If we've seen all of the white but only half of the black, then our centre is going to be incorrectly set up a little on the white side. Again, this is a nice idea to entertain but we need a practice to understand and live it.

Here is a simple but powerful practice to refine the physical centring: take our standing posture from the explanation above, with everything set up as centred as possible. Without changing the posture, shift the weight as far forward onto the toes as you can. Feel that the more you go towards the extreme of the toes, the more tension is necessary to hold you up. Stay at the extreme and feel this tension become more obvious. Return slowly, smoothly and as precisely as you can to the centre. Feel that as you approach the centre, the whole body begins to relax more and more (keep your posture though!). Then we take it backwards onto the heels and we see again that the more you go towards the extreme of the heel, the more tension is needed. Once again, we return to the centre and we can relax.

Now we also have an opportunity to see if we over or undershot the centre. Every time we return from the extremes, we have an opportunity to be more refined with where we settle in-between. You can further refine this exercise by progressively reducing how far you venture towards either extreme: you can go halfway to the toes, then return, then halfway to the heels, then return, or two centimetres towards the toe, back to the centre, then two centimetres towards the heel, then back. The smaller the distance, the more precisely you have to be at the centre upon your return, otherwise you're just wobbling around in one of the extremes. The amount you can deeply relax while maintaining a very strong structure will be reflective of how close you are. To confront the reality of how relaxed you are, you can do this exercise until you're as precise as you can be and then stand for a long time (30 minutes should be enough, although far more is possible). If you have any sense of pressure anywhere on the foot, parts of your leg falling asleep, or any other points of pressure like this anywhere in the body, it means you're not quite there yet. No problem, just keep practising!

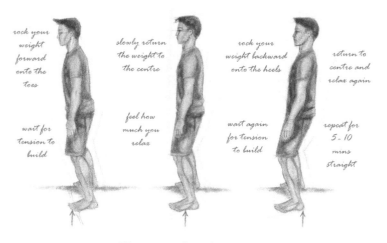

rock your weight forward onto the toes

wait for tension to build

slowly return the weight to the centre

feel how much you relax

rock your weight backward onto the heels

wait again for tension to build

return to centre and relax again

repeat for 5 - 10 mins straight

Figure 13 — Centring exercise

This particular exercise going forward and back is a staple in Da Xuan, but it can be easily translated to other areas of the body such as bending the knees too much then straightening them too much, or hinging the hips (as if you were sitting in a chair) then standing upright (which would require significant glute activation), or moving the head between poke neck and military neck. Whatever the case, the key ingredients are to notice the tension increasing as you approach whichever extreme, and to make a point of returning to the centre as precisely as you can and noticing the relaxation.

As I mentioned earlier, establishing the centre is a way of fusing the opposites by bringing awareness to the space which is in-between and connecting them. You will find in the beginning that the centre is vague, more like a region than a specific point. Having a vague centre creates an abyss between the opposites that is difficult to traverse. It leads to conflict between opposites and a fixation on one extreme or the other. To be truly centred is to fuse the opposites and thus open the potential for either or both to occur at any given moment. Training the physical centre for a few minutes a day is enough to begin with. Living in a body that is centred and thus whole is a deeply relaxing, rich and rewarding experience that is well worth the investment of daily practice.

CENTRING BELIEFS AND BEHAVIOURS

If we now translate this idea of 'uniting the opposites' to the arena of beliefs, ideas and behaviours, we can see some very interesting patterns occurring and sticking points that can become problems if left unattended. You can use any pair of opposites but let's start with a very broad example: indulging versus suppressing. Modern society and global culture at this point is one of suppressed emotions. In fact, it's almost as if the mark of the global culture is 'keeping it together', as if suppressing our emotions to get on with work or our meeting or whatever is a far more 'civilised' response. People will habitually apologise if they let slip a bit of anger or sadness, covering their emotional face with their hands and taking many other automated activities of suppression. It is definitely not cool to be emotional in a work situation or at any other time unless we are locked in a room away from everyone. Even at a funeral people engage in a mighty effort to not let their deep grief come out. If one were to wail loudly at a funeral, it would be as if they were 'making a scene' and everyone would rush to do everything possible to make them stop.

Many people recognise the problem of suppression, and a typical response to this recognition is to switch the polarity and go into complete indulgence. There are new-age fads where people recoil against the suppression of society and indulge any and every emotion that comes their way, losing their composure at the drop of a hat, constantly crying or raging and excusing themselves with talk about spirituality and expressing themselves. This is still a skipping record – it's just stuck in the opposite groove. When one has a clear centre, then there is the full possibility of organic emotional expression at the correct time without becoming addicted to either indulging intense emotions or suppression. A good sign that a response is centred is that it occurs simply and completely – after it is done there is no desire to relive it nor will we dwell on what happened. Another good sign of a centred approach is that it is not premeditated and is purely a present moment, a conscious response to what's happening right then and there.

Because it can't be premeditated, it's impossible to make yourself centred once a difficult situation is already transpiring – it's too late, and a desperate scramble back to centre can often unbalance the equation even more. We need to prepare by taking some time for practices that will push us consciously towards being more centred (striving for the perfect ideal of the Yang) and then allowing things to be as they are so the unconscious can catch up (accepting the imperfect reality of the Yin). With practice like this, the centred responses will naturally begin to occur more frequently – a good sign that the unconscious is actually being trained! Another strategy that I have found useful is to simply notice indulging or suppressing behaviours. To notice these patterns without blaming ourselves or giving ourselves credit for how clever we are for noticing, is a powerful centring practice. It's pure and curious awareness without judgement. We just notice as many times as we need to: 'How interesting, there it is again, it happened again'. We want to notice the reality without layering thoughts such as, 'It should have happened some other way', on top of what happened – no amount of arguing with what has already happened will change the reality that it happened.

Tension, Relaxation and Circulation

Let us now return the discussion to the physical. The physical is tangible – we can easily see and feel it – and so it's a good place to begin exploring the centre (as already discussed) and the fusion of opposites. We can investigate some basic opposites such as the relationship between 'tension and relaxation' or the relationship between 'strength and weakness'. In my own investigations, I became fascinated with exploring how relaxed I can become, while still remaining usefully strong, and whether anything can be done about all the excessive tension that we carry around with us as adults.

My fascination began, as far as I can recall, upon feeling the tissue quality of my first teacher, Wang Laoshi. His soft tissue (the red muscles and white connective tissue) did not feel like any adult I had felt at the time. The quality was much more like that of a baby or a cat. It was kind of squishy and I could palpate straight to the bone at many points on his body. By all appearances, the parts I did not palpate held this quality too. The kicker was that, unlike many noodle-esque people I had met who are soft-but-not-in-the-good-way, this suppleness was matched by his way more than reasonable strength. He had strength and relaxation and could express these two qualities simultaneously. An embodied union of opposites if I ever saw one! He could also, at will, flex the squishiness away and his skin would feel something like hardwood to the touch. It is very strange to feel such things in an adult and I can count on my hands the amount of people I have met besides him who have these qualities since then (most of them in the Da Xuan school).

At some point the idea arose in me: 'Could I train this body to be of such quality that a massage therapist could not find anything to work on?' It's a lofty ideal that is probably unattainable, but that has not prevented me from trying and making some serious inroads into the matter. The principles that I danced around during my explorations were outlined explicitly in Da Xuan, which helped tremendously. Let's have a look at them now:

- Tension blocks circulation and by extension our capacity to feel

- Tension protects weakness

- Long term (chronic) tension falls away from conscious awareness.

Circulation is pretty important – without it we will die. New and fresh in, old and stale out. We eat fresh food and breathe in fresh air and we excrete the used/stale food and breathe out the stale air. The various organic fluids bring fresh nutrients and oxygen to the far corners of the body, removing the waste products. Keeping these fluids moving through *all* corners of the body is crucial to health. In fact, many traditional systems of medicine (including the Da Xuan tradition of Daoist Medicine) have the idea that if everything is perfectly circulating then you are free of disease. It's an ideal that we can move closer and closer towards through practice, and in my experience doing so has an accelerating and cumulative effect on feeling and relaxation.

Circulation is a thing that is changing regularly. Change, change, change of a constant but shifting and new kind. This means it brings feeling and awareness of what's going on. Worse circulation = less feeling; better circulation = more feeling. You can try this for yourself: slap your hand hard on the table and then look at it and feel it. The new stimulus makes the hand go red from new blood and various other bodily substances (increased circulation), and you can feel it a lot more clearly (increased awareness). You might have seen Chinese folks out in the park walking around while firmly patting themselves all over. It's a practice called *Pāidǎ* and amongst other benefits, it stimulates the circulation. Western Olympic lifters use a similar principle, brushing down their whole body with a steel brush until all the skin is rosy red with increased circulation. They are able to feel their body more completely and as a result tend to have better performance in their lifting.

Even with such a cursory glance at the topic, it's easy to see that improving our circulation has many benefits. I'll use the image of a sponge to give an impression of the relationship we have between tension in the soft tissues and circulation. If you held a sponge in a running river it would slowly fill up with water, and new water would be moving through the entire sponge. Squeeze the sponge and the water inside is squeezed out, and new water is blocked from going inside. The inside of the squeezed parts would either dry up or contain trapped water which starts to go stale. Release the squeeze and the relaxation of the sponge would drag fresh and new water through its interior and clean out the water that was trapped inside. So, the squeezing (tension) itself is not a problem and in fact very beneficial when used in the right way.

Keeping tension on the other hand is not so good. If the sponge were to remain squeezed indefinitely, the trapped water would slowly become stagnant and stale, various lifeforms that enjoy swamp-like conditions would begin to party and multiply and sooner or later (read sooner) this part of the sponge will end up either gross and sludgy or, where there is no water, dry and crusty. Using this image to consider the soft tissues of our body we can see that it is in our best interests to keep all the muscles undulating between a contracted and a deeply relaxed state. In other words, get rid of all the chronic or held tension. They are the 'skipping record' of the physical body.

This is where we run into a bit of a conundrum. Tension is a mechanism in the body used by an amazing, unconscious biological intelligence to protect damaged, bottlenecked and weakened parts of our system – parts that are not capable of producing or receiving much force. Another image gives you an impression of this function: when the body is damaged in some way, the tension that arises is akin to a host of guards that are called in. Their job is to surround the weak point with a Spartan-like shield wall that takes all the forces that come through that area until the weakness is strong once more. This is a wonderful response that allows us to recover quickly after injury — without it, the weak point would be torn apart and mutilated the next time a significant force came through the area.

The body gains strength from exposure to the right amount of stress and force. This force must occur within a Goldilocks-like spectrum: too little and it will atrophy and worsen, too much and it will break. So weak areas need to be gradually exposed to more and more force, and for them to be exposed they need the guarding tension to progressively stand down. If you put too much force through the area too soon or convince too many of the guards to stand down thereby exposing and overwhelming the weak point, the body is going to (properly) respond by redeploying the protective tension and possibly even doubling or tripling the guard. Repeat this too many times and you dramatically increase the strength of the guards (tension) and simultaneously reduce the likelihood of getting the guards to stand down at all (relaxing). The body remembers that the last time it stood down the guard things went horribly wrong and doesn't want a repeat mistake — fair enough too!

When we look at this from the perspective of bodily awareness, this tension is a big source of our inability to feel what is happening in our body. Our minds are constantly bombarded with way too much information. To organise it so it doesn't overwhelm us, the mind will push things that don't change out of conscious awareness and into the realm of the unconscious – business as usual. Things that are changing regularly then have space to come to the forefront of our awareness so we can consider the change and adapt as necessary. If we want to be able to feel our body fully, we need the circulation to be free moving so that it keeps all corners of the body constantly changing and therefore in the awareness. If the guarding tension is fixed (not changing) and is also stopping the weak point from changing, then there will be a blank spot in our feeling.

We see here that the issue of tension is not that it exists, but that it can get stuck in the system – the guards can end up permanently on duty. This not only takes a significant amount of personal resources to maintain, but as we also saw, cuts off the weak links from circulation. It stays there out of sight and mind, sucking up resources – especially if the guard has been tripled a few times. Except that it's not out of sight at all, rather it is likely contributing directly and indirectly to many problems common amongst our chronically over-tensioned population (a population which also has a big problem with facing our shadows/weaknesses – coincidence?). I have often accidentally and indirectly sorted out problems, mine or someone else's, by simply focusing on removing seemingly unrelated excessive tension and strengthening the weak links.

APPROACH

A strategy to resolve this problem includes a two-fold approach:

1. Convince the guards to stand down (relax protective tension)

2. Progressively and gradually strengthen all the weak links until such time as a maximal force through the area doesn't invite the guards back.

We have to work on strength *and* relaxation at the same time. Union of opposites. Centring. Why? If you only work on relaxation techniques, you may convince the guards to stand down but you won't bring enough, or any, force through the weak link to stimulate it to become strong again. This means that as soon as force—especially chaotic force—is reintroduced to the area, the tension guard will simply be re-established or the structure will fail. Inversely, if you work only on traditional strengthening techniques, the body will (rightfully) select the strongest pathways to perform the task and reinforce them further, which will route the force via the outside of the shield wall rather than through the weak link. Basically, you turn your guard into The Mountain from *Game of Thrones*—definitely the undead version from the later seasons—and, well, you'll have about as much luck convincing him to stand down as Qyburn did (who ended up dead, for those who have not seen it).

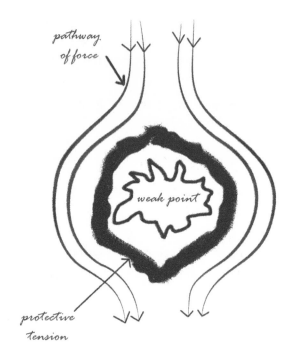

pathway
of force

weak point

protective
tension

Figure 14 — Diagram of force being routed around the weak link

Now, this does not mean you can't get super-strong by normal strengthening techniques, it's just that by doing so you will progressively make it more difficult to access and repair the weak points buried deep in the system under strong tension. You widen the gap between the weak and strong and create a divide between these opposites. Depending how much you do, it slows or completely stops the process of union – the body really has an incredible capacity to avoid using these weak points so the method used to expose them must have a way of cornering the weak link and leaving it no other choice but to gradually strengthen. If you have The Mountain there, you have another choice.

TRAINING STRENGTH AND RELAXATION SIMULTANEOUSLY

Relaxation techniques where there is no need for structure or strength can provide very useful temporary relief letting the guard take a rest. On the flip side, training strength in the already-strong pathways appears to make one strong at the cost of hiding the tension and weak links more thoroughly. This kind of 'big strength' training will stop being counter-productive to our process of union only when the most effective pathways of the bodily structure have been cleared of weak links, that is, when you have a good structure. This means you are free of compensation patterns and the body operates as an efficient single unit that doesn't fight itself or gravity. Centred and united. In the Da Xuan tradition, we work at things in a specific order: strengthen weak links and unite the body *first*—which isn't a '6-week-abs' transformation and requires patience— and only after this is done, you can work on the 'big strength'. If you've already tried some of the physical exercises from Chapter 2, you might have noticed how it very quickly lights up and starts working whatever weak points you might have. It's hard work, but simultaneously relaxing, especially at the end. The longer you train and the better at it you get, you resolve more weak points and the more relaxing the practice becomes. Practising a single exercise for thirty minutes straight or more without moving is not such a big deal when the weak points are mostly resolved, and the structure is pretty centred.

The concept of the structure that I've mentioned here is layered. A strong structure is a frame that will hold the body up with minimal need for tension in the soft tissue to act as support.

It is the strength of the well-aligned skeleton combined with reinforced joints that allows the soft tissues to relax. It needs to be particularly aligned to gravity, which is a constant force, and be able to respond accordingly to any other external force, reorganising as needed to be a good conductor of the multiple vectors of incoming force (such as those coming from another person). Hidden tension caused by weak links distorts this alignment, which *increases* the amount of strength you need to do any given activity.

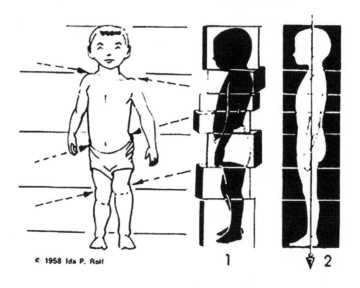

© 1958 Ida P. Rolf

1

2

Figure 15 — Ida Rolf's stacked blocks

The vision from Ida Rolf shown above shows this idea well from the perspective of gravity. Ida Rolf's system of soft tissue therapy, called Rolfing, was revolutionary in its approach to organising the bodily structures to work *with* gravity rather than against it. She compared our bodily structure to blocks or a Jenga tower to show that when the 'blocks' of our structure are stacked unevenly, gravity makes the whole thing unstable. Unlike Rolfing, however, we must also look at progressively strengthening this good alignment so that it works in increasingly complex and demanding situations, against other incoming forces, and making it dynamic so that it maintains integrity even as we move about, or someone or something tries to interfere with it. Experientially, this means that the effort is perceived more and more as 'coming from the centre', and as mentioned above, the centre is a funhouse of all kinds of paradox with both opposites being able to be expressed at once. It makes sense that the simultaneous expression of strength and relaxation comes from there too.

A BALANCED PRACTICE

Remember that intention dictates results. Your practice should generally be backed by the intention to maintain the exercise's movement and structural/postural points and simultaneously relax as completely as possible. This skill always involves a little bit of back-and-forth between being too relaxed, where the desired posture collapses a little or you lose the motion, and being too tense. It is something you can only refine over time, and more precision is necessary to find some of the deeper tensions that hang around the organs, nervous system, or deep in the emotional and mental landscapes.

We want to work in both a specific way with exercises that target known weak links, and in a global way with exercises that address the entire system at once so that the elusive tensions and subtle compensation patterns that hide out in the shadows and escape detection can be resolved too. We also want to balance the analysis of all of this with the good-old-fashioned advice of 'don't think, just do'.

Over-thinking and over-analysis create their own kind of mental tension and, in bad cases, can make you neurotic about something. Analysis and intellectual consideration create the structure of our training so are necessary to stop our training becoming noodle-like. Taken too far though, they make our minds excessively rigid – a condition that is rife in the modern world. To prevent unnecessary tension in the mental space, we need times in our practice where we don't think, ask 'why', correct or analyse, but rather relax the mind as much as we can while we train. We need to spend about half our practice time following the wise words of Shia Labeouf: DO IT!

CONFRONTING THE UNCOMFORTABLE

It's useful to remind ourselves here that to get to a state of deep relaxation, we must address the weak points and that is not generally going to be a 'fun' experience. Often, revealing the weak link can make things feel worse than they were before, when we didn't know about it. How bad the original issue was, the related emotional states, and the length of time it has been quarantined from our awareness are all factors that affect both the sensory experience and the duration needed to resolve the issue. The discovery of a previously unknown weak link can often be paired with some kind of intense and noxious sensation.

I want to take a moment to reinforce this next point: to strengthen this weak link does not mean that we make the noxious sensations disappear. It means that we want to transform the sensation from noxious to something more manageable or pleasant. Remember, if it's circulating, we should be able to feel something!

Ignorance is not bliss. If the sensation disappears then you have simply reinstated (or in some cases strengthened) the guard and plunged the weak link back into the shadows of the unconscious. Once a noxious link is discovered, we should *not* aim to make the rather intense, uncomfortable sensation 'go away'.

Noxious sensation is superior to no sensation!!!

We want to keep the sensation around and get it to participate as much as possible in what's going on, without further irritating it, until it finds resolution.

This is a fine line to walk. A mistake that would plunge one suddenly into the wrong side of the equation can drag us back to the beginning or an even worse position. Hence, we work in a slower but less risky fashion. The Da Xuan tradition talks about training to a light sweat, with a perceived effort of about seventy percent of our maximum. Light or medium intensity motions that are regularly repeated are ideal here, just as they are in Western rehabilitation models – only these aren't exercises we do to get back to our 'real' training, this *is* the real training. A long, slow 'juicing' of the weak link of all of its accumulated sludge until it's back to fresh and full capacity is what we're after. To go back to the image of the swampish sponge, we want to continuously and gently squeeze and release it until it is clear of all swamp-like materials and only fresh water is moving through. The felt sensation at the point of resolution can be very close to the feeling of a clean river running through the affected area. It's subtle, but very pleasant. The transformation of the noxious sensations into this clean and fresh sensation is one of the good signs of successful resolution and restoration of circulation. We must then rinse and repeat (pun intended) this process with the next hidden tension and weak link.

This is quite the rabbit hole to venture down. Resolution of one tension and weak link can reveal more tension and weakness that was hidden deeper in the system. This is a positive result, as we are learning more about ourselves. To clean it all out we must go right down to the very centre – literally all the small tensions near the bones, organs, nervous system sheaths and so on (which will finally allow a true union). It's a long process and if you want to do any more than a superficial job it becomes necessary to put down many activities that would go against it, or risk stretching the process out by decades and decades. The good news is that even though it takes some time, when it's done it's done. Even in the case of re-injury, being armed with the skills to start resolving it immediately means things don't really get stuck in the system again. In my personal experience the (progressively more) united expression of effortless, relaxed strength has been infinitely more interesting and wonderful to live with and have readily available than the raw strength I had worked on in the past.

The Two-Way Street of Relationship

We live in a demanding time and culture. I don't mean

demanding as in 'difficult for us', although that is quite true as well, but rather I mean that we are constantly demanding that things be a certain way. Another way to put this is that we like to impose our ideas upon basically every aspect of the world. I could very easily launch into commentary and analysis of our culture here but that has been done to death already and I'm much more interested in a more immediate, intimate relationship which we can seriously impact – that is, our relationship with our bodies.

I speak here both from my own experience with my body and from observing how I see many others relate to their bodies. I spent a great deal of my own practice history making significant demands of my body and imposing particular ideas of how I wanted my body to be (as well as doing the same thing to my mind, but that is a whole other story!). For a long time, I was constantly insisting that it be a particular way – stronger, more flexible, more supple, more coordinated, less painful, and so on. The list of demands was endless and as soon as something was achieved, several more things would be added. I have observed that this is a typical relationship that those in the realms of performance and well-being have with their body.

On the other side of this spectrum are those who appear to simply want their body to be quiet already and leave them in peace. It is a situation not unlike someone getting a pet dog, completely ignoring it, and then wondering why it spends the majority of its time howling, whining or barking. Attempts to pacify the cries may lead to a short period of silence but will ultimately lead to more and more outbursts. The only difference here is that we didn't have a choice about getting a body.

LEARNING THE LANGUAGE OF SENSATION

Whether we like it or not, we are all in a relationship with our bodies and our minds. We can allow the strange ideas of our mind to whip the body into whichever shape or state is currently 'most desirable' according to the cultural mind, turning the body into an excellent servant that will obey our every command. But the mind's attention span is short, and it is never satisfied for long, so this approach ultimately leaves one chasing phantoms. From a performance perspective this clearly can and does work. One may even say it's necessary if you want to be competitive. But I am not interested in relationships of slavery, even if it means the world's best performance.

I found it far more interesting to learn the language of the body: sensation. Like learning any language, it was (and still is) quite a mammoth task – think months and years rather than days and weeks. Sensations are not as clear-cut as words in their meaning and the body is not really governed by the same logic, reason and rationale as the mind. In the beginning there wasn't much to work with. There seemed to only be two sensations: the normal, neutral body (good!) or intense sensation that was generally labelled 'pain' (bad!).

My practice began to reveal something wonderful, however. An entire spectrum of sensations became ever-more apparent, ranging from the most subtle to the most super intense. And very slowly it became clear that just because a sensation was extremely subtle did not necessarily mean it was a 'good' sensation, and just because a sensation was extraordinarily intense did not mean it was 'bad'. On the contrary, some of the most severe warnings came through subtly and some of the loudest, most intense sensations were like the body shouting for joy and wanting to keep going. Very few of the multitudes of sensations actually implied immediate danger.

With practice we can become more and more proficient in understanding the sensations of the body and what they mean. But as we saw, the mind works with trickery and deceit. In a subtle subterfuge, it can use this new capacity to speak the body's language to order the body about in a more efficient way and continue imposing on it. Learning the language of the body is only half of the puzzle it would seem.

LISTENING

The purpose of language is communication, and communication is not super useful if no one is listening. If we want a good relationship with our body, we must learn how to communicate with it more effectively, and that means *listening* to it. A body, especially a neglected body, has a whole host of its own requests and needs. Needs that are often vastly different from those imagined by the mind. Listening does not mean the mind is waiting for its turn to impose nor does it necessarily mean offering up solutions to whatever is 'said'. Sometimes, often, the body just needs to have the sensations allowed into full awareness. Awareness through and through, without our mind trying to resolve them like a puzzle – not unlike how a good counsellor genuinely listens to their patient's experience of tragedy and suffering. You may be surprised what lies at the eye of the storm when the body is giving all kinds of intense and painful sensations, if only you would pay close attention to it instead of scrambling for any way to make it stop.

Navigating this ground requires skill and the mind will often find ways to overlay its own agenda: *If I just listen long enough, this sensation of pain might go away* or *If I get good enough at listening than I can finally perform that skill that I always wanted.* The reality is that listening sometimes means compromise and not getting everything the mind wanted. Maybe the body doesn't want anything to do with whatever performance the mind is interested in, and maybe it never will want anything to do with that. Perhaps that pain coming from an old injury is there simply as a very loud request to pay attention to a neglected corner of the body which has long since been physically repaired.

Most of the exercises in the Da Xuan tradition can be viewed as ways of giving certain, often long-forgotten areas of the body a stage and a loudspeaker. This offers two opportunities. One is to learn what the vast array of sensations that may come forth mean and the other is an opportunity to simply listen. One of the most common questions I get asked is how long to do a certain exercise and I can feel the person just waiting for some more *ammunition of imposition*; another shiny new way of telling the body how we would like it to go about *bodying*. But we have another option too: we can listen to the body and let it go as long as *it* wants. If you really pay attention and listen, the body will very obviously tell you when it's done with a particular practice by simply ceasing it (without a thought on the matter – the body doesn't think after all, that's the mind). Of course, in the beginning we do not understand the language of the body so we throw an arbitrary number at the mind to keep it satiated while the body gets its chance to be front and centre for once.

It is amusing to watch the mind struggle with the intense sensations that the body is actually revelling in. Stay in any exercise for long enough to start to approach a threshold and the mind almost immediately pipes up (one of its finest tricks): *Nope, nope, nope, nope, nope, NOPE. WE ARE CERTAINLY GOING TO DIE IF WE STAY HERE FOR ONE SECOND LONGER*. But tune into the bodily sensations and it becomes apparent that a great shift and unravelling is occurring which the body likes very much, despite its intensity. Also, you don't die, so there's that little hiccup in the narrative of the thoughts. It is similar to many of the basic exercises: an intensity arrives almost immediately that the mind wants nothing to do with, but the body is quite enjoying and is very capable of proceeding with for a long time before it will stop. The gap between the mind giving up and the body needing to stop is far bigger than most suspect.

You also have the problem where many exercises (most of the basic exercises in Da Xuan, to be honest) are really dull for the mind. But the body is interested and wants to pursue them in depth. Boredom itself is only ever a state of mind, it is not something the body knows in any way. If boredom is making you want to stop, remember that this is a request of the mind, not of the body.

ATTITUDE

It's not really about *what* you are doing but rather *how* you are doing it. There is a big difference between this approach and the approach to regular physical practices. You could just as easily do any of the exercises I prescribe with an attitude of imposition and go for years without understanding this point at all. It's not that we don't want to impose upon the body ever again, but rather we are aiming to repair the balance of the relationship between the mind and the body. Again, we have a mixing and fusion of the opposites around a centre and an exchange in *both* directions. The body actually starts to become happy when this relationship becomes more of a two-way street, and will also be more inclined to participate without complaining and help when it can. This happiness presents itself as a wonderful song of sensations that will sing you through the day if you so let it – and warn you of possible problems approaching well in advance of their actualisation, if you are indeed listening.

The body will also begin to exhibit an irrational intelligence that is completely beyond the understanding of the reasonable and rational mind. Why and how are really not in the repertoire of the body and many things can be done without reason or rationality, simply because that's the way they get done. This physical intuition can appear on many levels. In my experience, I am often struck by how the body wants to do things in a particular way. It is an urge that appears without thought or an idea behind it. If someone were to ask me why I did that particular thing, the only honest answer I could give is 'I don't know', or at a stretch 'My body wanted to' (although this amounts to the mind acting like it has any idea about what went on). In retrospect, it becomes clear that these bodily actions have a tangible and sometimes extraordinary effect that would not have been possible if the mind took the lead.

This is not an invitation to constantly interrupt our practice to do pleasant waving motions that allow the mind to escape from its discomforts and confrontation with weakness. To do so is to avoid listening to the parts of the body that need listening to the most. We must respect the limitations set by our practice and the tradition and stay in our practice – it's a way of preventing the mind's subterfuge, as all of these ways to escape discomfort are part of the mind's bag of tricks. However, if we improve the relationship with our body *by way of* the limitations set out by our practice, the body shifts from being a slave to being an extraordinarily reliable friend, with whom you share a most intimate trust. This trust goes both ways and the body also begins to trust you which, as you can imagine, creates a huge potential for life to be a whole lot more colourful.

All you need is a willingness to actually go into your practice honestly. Drop every idea you have about how you think it's meant to be, or what other people think of what you're doing, do the exercises *as prescribed* and listen to your body. If you listen instead to thoughts and ideas about what is happening, you are not listening to the body. You must try to go directly to the sensation. Oh, and relax about it all. There's no sense in forcing a relationship to be immediately fruitful. Forcing it works in this situation about as well as forcing relationships with other people does (it doesn't work at all). Take your time, slow down, and enjoy the process of rediscovering a long-forgotten friend!

Opening the Potential

To remove the pressure of forcing our practice to be fruitful, we've got to learn how to stop trying so hard all the time, to let go and just do. We must regularly rest from the act of pressuring ourselves to produce results that we are not yet capable of, or ready for, which in an ironic twist actually prevents them from appearing. An effort is required but try too hard and you can create a kind of psychic desperation that brings along an incredible tension. You can see how this would not work so well when you are doing practices that are designed to relieve tension and inhibition rather than building on them.

Being myself a chronic victim of over-trying, I had to find a way to untangle this knot so as not to spend too many (more) years spinning my wheels. As I began to untangle it for myself, I also had to find a way to teach that didn't entangle my students in the same knot. It is a puzzling task because on the one hand if there is no effort at all, there is no movement to the next stage, and on the other hand if there is too much effort, it will knot everything up and stagnate the practice. For a teacher, this means knowing when and what to cue and when to leave the student in the dark, knowing the point when more will just confuse them further. But the student has a role to play here too. I suspect solving this conundrum itself will be one of the stages that almost everyone has to progress through at some point in their practice so I thought that sharing some of my current insights into this topic may prove useful.

SETTING THE STAGE

I orient my practice around a concept that I call opening the potential. It is an attitude we bring to our practice where instead of making an effort to make the change happen, we instead make an effort to create a big potential *for* it to happen. It's a small but crucial change in how we orient ourselves if we want to move towards balance.

Allow me to beat a metaphor to death to explain the idea in more depth. Imagine you are interested in seeing the greatest performer of all time on stage. You have ideas about what a great performance might look like, but you don't know where the performer is or how to contact them or even who they are or what they can *really* do. You devise a plan to create your own stage in the hopes it will attract the performer. Every day you set your stage up in the best way that your resources will allow you, and you put a little sign out front encouraging people to bring their greatest performances. The beginning is slow, but eventually a passing hobo sees the stage with the sign you have put up and jumps up to perform. It's not that great but it's a start. You continue setting your stage each day. Some days no one comes by. Slowly but surely the word gets out and, as you get better at setting your stage, you attract more interesting performers. You begin to notice which things the interesting performers prefer to have on stage and which things are no good. You change your stage, alter it here and there. Better and better performers appear. You still have your quiet days where no one comes along but you set the stage up anyway just in case. Sometimes these quiet days run back to back. Where are all the performers? You have no clue but you keep at it anyway. After some years, your experience of how to set the stage has grown considerably, it is slowly becoming quite a remarkable stage. At one point a performer arrives and delivers a performance the likes of which you have never seen! Was that it?!? Perhaps. Or perhaps not. You continue setting the stage, never quite sure if the next performer will be even more impressive and interesting than the last, all the while progressively making the stage more and more suitable for the most amazing performances. As the years pass, the performers that grace the stage are far beyond the first dazzling performance that you originally thought was the best. You also still get your fair share of hobos and quiet days, but you set the stage anyway just because you enjoy setting it up and seeing what comes of it.

To open the potential means to set the stage (which is your practice) in the best way you know how and then not be too concerned with who appears or doesn't appear (the results of the practice). It's an attitude of using the practice to keep the aperture of potential open and progressively widening it rather than worrying about making the potential manifest. To stop the practice would mean to reduce the potential to almost nil. To use the practice to force the potential to manifest is like constantly adjusting your stage without rest – it leaves little time or space for the performer to actually perform. An uphill battle at best and a waste of energy that results in nothing, at worst.

In Da Xuan we say that you can only work on the Yang (the process) and that it's impossible to work directly with the Yin (manifestation of the process). By adjusting the Yang, the Yin will inevitably follow. Improve the process and the results of the process will improve too.

Our effort is most usefully directed at maintaining and improving the potential with whatever resources we happen to have available on that day. We must balance the technical corrections with a playful approach of just doing the practice without correction. We spend a bit of time each day setting our stage but, at some point, we have to accept that it's about as set as it's going to get that day and allow whatever acts that appear the space to do their thing (or not). Too much time in the technical adjustments brings about a neuroticism. Too little effort, and nothing will happen. It's a fine line to walk but we can only improve with practice!

DRAWING ON TRADITION

It is useful to understand how to set the stage and which things have worked for others in the past and why. It is here that a teacher and tradition can be invaluable. They are the guides who draw on vast experience to help you along your way, point you towards other possibilities and stop you from going down dead ends. A good teacher and tradition will also allow room for and even encourage your individuality and the possibility of you bringing something new that was not previously known, a nice balance between new and old.

This way of approaching a practice hints at a practical expression of the emptiness and mystery talked about in many spiritual traditions too. When you leave the potential open, you leave room for things not yet known to appear, or for things that you thought would happen in one way to happen in another. If you do this for long enough, something may occur that might just blow your mind wide open. Or it may not. That's the quality of mystery – you really never know and never can know. What you can be sure of is that if you try to force the results every day, you will probably not get the results you are after and you will certainly shut down the possibility of the unexpected happening. If you think you know what the performance that day will be like and only book your stage out to the performer who can do that, you're stifling the potential of the unknown.

What we end up with when we keep our efforts on the potential rather than the manifestations is a practice that is both very relaxed and always growing. Every day presents an opportunity to do our practice in a way that's a little more informed by experience than the last, and a little closer to an ideal that can never be reached – after all, how do you prepare for that which you do not know is coming? Even so, we can relax knowing that we did what we could in the best way we knew how on any given day. Whether the mysterious and wondrous results of the practice show up that day is not at all up to us. And who knows, maybe the hobo is hiding something quite magnificent under his mundane outward appearance after all and you just had to watch him for the 300th time to catch it!

Light and Shadow

In white-washed, tube-lit corridors and antiseptic cubicles,
Where does the mystery lie?
Under overheating, buzzing ballasts,
How can serenity arise?

~John O'Donohue

Celtic poet John O'Donohue had a great passage in his series of talks called 'Anam Cara'. He talked of the modern mind being like a neon light that wants to cast its brightness into every shadow 'to unriddle and control the unknown.' We can see this reflected in the way our houses and streets are lit up at night by bright lights, and in the bright sterility of our schools and clinical rooms. But, as O'Donohue observes, the experience of the brightness of a hospital clinic or a classroom full of neon lights and stainless-steel benchtops is one that is cold and harsh. He goes on to compare the neon clinical environment to the warmth, hospitality and welcoming of a candle-lit room or the traditional *hearth* of a house where the living area gathers around a fireplace.

Bringing this image to mind, we are immediately met with a scene of light (Yang) and shadow (Yin) mixing and interacting, rather than that of the Yang dominating in the clinic. The flicker of the flame occasionally casting light where there was shadow, and occasionally retreating to let the shadow come back in. The dance and play of the light and dark speaks to our hearts, and it is no coincidence that heart and hearth are almost identical words. We also see that we don't want the light to go out *completely*, only that it shares its space and time with the dark.

There is a practical element here where we could (and probably should) go about reintroducing this dance to our evenings, turning off the screens and bright lights in favour of a soft, warm and *moving* light that allows shadows to play during the twilight hours before we sleep. I dare say this would also bring about a huge positive shift if implemented in our schools, hospitals and workplaces.

In the Da Xuan tradition, we are confronted with the same dance. *Dà Xuán* literally means 'Big Secret'. When we start practice, we quickly find out that how we thought it would turn out is, in fact, nothing at all like how it *does* turn out. Soon enough it becomes apparent that you could never have predicted how it would go, even in your wildest dreams. It's not that after some amount of time you have gathered enough knowledge and experience to know what's going to come — this would be the neon view of things. It's more that as your understanding increases from practice, you start to be in a much better relationship with what you *don't know*. There is a respect and awe for the mystery of the never-ending depth of the tradition and for life itself.

> *The teaching of the secret means that we are trying to teach something to you, to open up and reveal something hidden.*
>
> *Now, you might point out, if the secret is taught, it is no longer a secret. A revealed secret, it would seem, is an oxymoron.*
>
> *That would be so if we were discussing an artificial secret, one that is secret only because it is shrouded in secrecy, because others don't want you to find out. True secrets, even once*

taught, explained, illustrated, analysed and integrated into your consciousness, remain just as mysterious as before. No — vastly more mysterious, for as the island of knowledge expands, so too its beach upon the infinite sea of the unknowable.

~Rabbi Tzvi Freeman

As you practise and the light of knowledge flickers and reveals something new, so too does the play of shadows shroud something you *thought* you knew back into mystery. It's a moment of realising there is much more to this than meets the eye. There is an element of humility here too, as our small mind comes into harmony with something much greater than itself — an ever-deepening mystery that can never be entirely discovered.

I must point out here again that the idea of one not being more important than the other is crucial. We still need concepts to frame what we are doing, still have to study, learn new things, and have an ever-growing understanding of what's going on. To be completely in the dark is just as unbalanced as being flooded with too much light. It is the way the Yin and the Yang relate to each other, and the way we relate to their ebb and flow that allows us to come into wholeness and balance.

Stress & Personal Resources

When we are out of balance, we become stressed — a signal asking us to return to the centre if we can. Stress is the modern predator that has taken the place of beasts, plagues and inter-tribal violence. The great majority of people exist in a state of low to moderate stress all the time. Most of us have not experienced true deep relaxation since we were children. Our personal resources are drained by over-analysis, emotional instability, unnecessary excessive physical tension and sedentary lifestyles (which all go hand-in-hand). This lack of resources leaves us unable to properly digest emotions, trapping them in various aspects of our being. As this downward-spiral progresses over the course of our lives, we lose sight of what *relaxed* actually means. Instead, we exist on a spectrum that goes from 'very fucking stressed' to 'numb but still stressed' (which we may incorrectly label as relaxed).

Whether we are stressed or relaxed depends on the available energy and how close to 'empty' we go to complete whatever task is at hand. Not having enough energy to do tasks or digest emotions creates the imbalance. An exercise that is not overtly stressful (physically, emotionally or mentally) becomes progressively more so as we run out of steam. A simple math problem is difficult to solve when we are tired. It is agitating when we can't do what we know we should be able to do easily. A little emotional irritation that would not normally bother us when we have the energy to digest it becomes a complete meltdown when we are exhausted. As we free up energy locked in stasis by habits, and become more centred and expand our reserves via practice, we progressively get more relaxed and less stressed *because we have more energy*.

SPENDING AND REPLENISHING RESOURCES

How can we make more energy? We already talked about how the breath can bring in an enormous amount of energy, but it is useful to look a little more closely at how these resources are replenished and also how they are spent — after all, they are all we have to get through life. At the centre of it all is this magical process: we fuel ourselves by taking something that isn't us, bringing it inside us and then transforming it to something that is us. This also works in the opposite way: we take parts of us that are no longer needed and send them out into the world so they can be used by the other in some way. This circulating exchange is at the very foundation of all of life.

While there are plenty of more subtle ways we go about doing this, such as absorbing sunlight and other environmental energies (there are practices to improve these in the Da Xuan tradition, by the way), I want to look at the three primary fuels. We have the food that we eat, the liquids that we drink and the air that we breathe.

I already mentioned food a little earlier, but it's worth reiterating that we need to use some energy to digest and assimilate the food. This process can be improved with diets and practices that assist with digestion, but at some point there is only so much you can transform — after all, we can't just eat more to have more energy. Everyone would be familiar with the food coma, when you've eaten so much that the body needs to draw on more than its usual resources to process it and so you have to power down until that's done. It is useful to note that in traditional Chinese medicine, the stomach is linked directly to the rational, thinking mind (called the *Yi* — this is only one aspect of the mind in the Chinese system, there are many others). As well as bringing in more energy and reducing the digestive resource spend, eating a balanced Daoist diet has the potential to clear your mind and reduce over-thinking and worry. We can see here that the potential for increasing energy just by your diet is pretty good, but there's more that can be done.

FUEL EFFICIENCY

We can look at how we spend our fuel and where it might be possible to free up resources that are being used poorly or unnecessarily. I'll start with the obvious – the body. We need energy to move our body and run all the organic functions. Exercise is a wonderful way to make us breathe more than usual and also help push the circulation to the various corners of the body, generating a lot of energy for us. Unfortunately, it also spends a decent amount getting the job done, especially if you are uncentred and full of weak links and hidden tensions. Physical work can be done any old way and it will pretty much work the same each time: if you do too much you'll be more exhausted than when you started, too little won't add enough to the tank, and just right will leave you feeling vibrant and energised. There's a sweet spot for the intensity of practice that, with experience, you can start to hit regularly, and this is a nice thing to find. The more familiar we are with centring the easier it is to hit the nail on the head. To repeat the traditional guideline, try to get to a light sweat and about a seventy percent perceived rate of work. You want to try and hit this Goldilocks zone every day during your formal practice.

From the perspective of the personal resources, a great deal of fuel is spent maintaining protective tension in the body. This cost is MASSIVE. It is typically hidden tension but as we talked about earlier, our practices can work to simultaneously reveal and relax the tension and restore strength (and circulation) to the areas being protected so they can function for themselves once more. When this can be achieved while hitting the sweet spot of intensity, you start to get a cumulative effect: energy gained from the physical work is stacked on top of energy freed from fuelling unneeded tension. The more resources that are gathered, the more that become available for the restoration and so the better that process works. So on it goes in an ever increasing feedback loop. This feedback loop is what we want to develop with the basic physical practices of Da Xuan.

Once we move into the arena of mind and emotions, we have a whole new order of potential to free up unnecessary energy use. I won't delve too deeply into the topic of emotions for now, which is a minefield too vast to address properly in a book. I will say that negative emotions require a significant amount of energy to digest and if that energy is not available it can often lead to plenty of problems.

RELAXING THE MIND

The mind presents some very interesting possibilities. Cognition of all kinds (thinking, accessing memory, focus, intention, concentration, fabrication of ideas and so on) generally consumes a large quantity of energy. This is obvious to anyone who has tried to do any of these things while they are exhausted – it's quite difficult. There is also the layer of maintaining belief structures. These tend to be with us our whole lives until by way of practice (or occasionally blind luck) we are suddenly unburdened by them. Anyone who has been through such a thing can attest to the huge release of effort and subsequent feeling of relief that comes from freeing yourself of things you didn't even know were weighing you down.

When we use the perspective of personal resources to look at what our practices are doing, we can see a few things. Firstly, we see that there is quite a distinct difference between breathing practices, which will add to our energy reserves, and practices of concentration, focus, imagination and other mental activities which will spend energy. Certain mental practices can lead to the destruction of belief structures or a calmer mind which can reduce the spend in amazing ways, freeing energy you already had to be used elsewhere but never adding to the energy reserves. Learning to relax the mind means that we don't have to spend valuable resources constantly reorienting it back to the task at hand or creating unnecessary chains of thoughts or projections of images or anything else. It's not increasing your pay packet, but rather decreasing how much of your pay packet you spend on useless things. You might be surprised how much you really have spare!

With this perspective we can start to make sense of the general structure of practice used in the Da Xuan tradition. In one way, you could see the first years of practice as sorting out your personal resources. We separate the practices of the mind, breath and body because they achieve different things. With the practices of the mind, we work on getting to know our mind, how it operates, and how to keep it focused on specific tasks for long periods of time or simply teach it to relax when thinking isn't needed. It's a lot like training a hyperactive puppy. While the result is a relaxed mind that can focus properly and is generally available with ever more resources being liberated, the process can often be exhausting. We are purposefully spending our resources to achieve a more efficient and effective baseline for the mind that doesn't use so much fuel.

INCREASING RESOURCES

Breathing practices improve intake and assimilation. How can we add the most resources while spending the least? Essentially, we want the mind and body doing as little as possible. This is hard enough to do on its own. To train it simultaneously with the focus practices of the mind and/or postural practices of the body is going to be incredibly difficult if not impossible for the beginner. When we separate these practices, we create feedback loops that complement each other. Training the body to be coordinated and free of excess tension liberates resources. Structure and grounding help us to keep the body still for long periods of time without needing to spend much holding us upright. This, in turn, helps us do our breathing and mental practices without interference or unnecessary spending. Learning to relax the mind helps us maintain a relaxed focus in our breathing and bodily practices, which makes each of those practices more effective. Breathing without spending creates more resources to be used for training the body and mind – and on it goes.

This model of practice creates an exponential possibility to increase our personal resources. At some point in the practice, we begin to go into excess. We have more than enough fuel to operate in life and deal with every and any challenge that might arise. We are no longer spending our fuel on fighting ourselves and so the resources we add with our practice then begin to accumulate. I will emphasise again: challenges only become problems when we are short on the resources to deal with them. We then have trouble completing simple tasks and it can eventually lead to a meltdown or, if we are constantly exposed to this over a long period of time, any number of the common chronic issues such as cancer, autoimmune disease, dementia, or diabetes.

This alone is reason enough to practise in this way. To add to this, when we go into a large excess, we start to be able to use it to transform ourselves in ways that are not possible otherwise. We can digest bigger shocks and so face aspects of ourselves and our world that are otherwise difficult to face without being driven to a breakdown or burrowing into deeper denial. In the Da Xuan tradition we say that we want to be happy first and only then do we face reality. In my experience, happiness doesn't come from removing challenges in our lives but from having the resources to confront them completely. When we don't have sufficient resources to confront a challenge completely, it's as if our organism knows and so works to quarantine the problem in the unconscious (physical, emotional, mental) until such time as we have enough spare fuel to face it again.

You can probably imagine how this would stack up over a lifetime of increasing stress and avoiding challenges. We are living in a time where the cultural body values comfort and ease, finding every possibility to go away from the challenges of life and towards convenience or feigned happiness. Much of our technology is based around getting a machine or tool to solve problems for us. We have become the masters of avoiding the struggles of life, but in doing so we have robbed ourselves of the very thing that makes us grow. It's not that we have to throw away everything we've made. But perhaps now it is time we stop running, gather our energy, and use our vitality to turn and face the world fully, both the good and the bad, so that we may feel our ever-growing aliveness once more.

A table of usage and generation which summarises these ideas on energetic usage can be found below.

Table 2: Energetic usage

Action	Energetic Usage
Thinking	• Uses a lot of energy.
Forcing specific focus and concentration	• Uses energy.
Relaxing the mind	• No energy generation but frees up energy from being used unnecessarily by the mind.
Emotions	• Digesting negative emotions uses energy.
Breathing	• Generates energy from external fuel, more generated when the exchange is felt more completely/consciously.
Food	• Generates energy from external fuel. • Uses energy for digestion.
Physical Action	• Generates energy by making you breathe more. • Uses energy to create motion and hold tension. • Motion assists in digestion, and circulation of organic fluids and energy.

Sleep

Sleep is a time for us to recover energy and digest the emotions of the day through dreaming. It is an obvious time for recuperation as the body and mind get a moment of respite and all of our thoughts about how we believe the world to be disappear into the void as the breathing continues to prepare enough energy for the next day.

Sleeping is *not* a time for relaxing. We must already be relaxed by the time we head to sleep. We need to wind the day down through a routine that sees us off to bed in an already relaxed state that will help us go straight into a good sleep.

Building a Sleep Routine

Find a way that you like to relax in the thirty to sixty minutes leading to your entry to the bed. Warm showers, baths, relaxing with a book, dim warm light (no flouro or cold/blue lights), no screens, and sitting by candlelight are all good options. Try to keep a few hours between eating and sleep if you can. Digesting food while sleeping will use resources that could otherwise be used for digesting emotions. Breathing practice right before bed is also a nice way to relax and wind down. Make sure to set your alarms before starting practice so you can get ready and go to bed without looking at a screen. Get a traditional alarm clock and leave your phone outside the bedroom.

Seeing the Mistake

'At the end of every day compose a list of the mistakes you have made that day. The day you don't find a mistake is the day you take a step back instead of a step forward.'
~Wang Laoshi

As with any endeavour, starting down this path of training, centring, uniting, building energy and all the rest can appear mighty confusing, and we are bound to make plenty of mistakes well before arriving at any kind of clarity about it all. My first teacher, Wang Laoshi, shared the above nugget of wisdom about mistakes with me in the early stages of my training, and we also have specific practices around this idea in the Da Xuan tradition. There is much to be gained from understanding the depth of what this really means. Unfortunately, our cultural body has a huge aversion to being wrong. We tend to force mistakes to be rectified immediately and reprimand the person who made it or we 'accept it' by pretending it doesn't exist, ignoring it and just hoping it will go away and not bother us. There is a third option: a centred response rather than a polarised one.

Seeing mistakes is how we learn. If you do something correctly the first time *you haven't actually learnt anything*. There is little point in just going about doing the things we can (or believe we can) already do – it is a huge stagnation and waste of our human potential. *Forcing* a mistake to be 'corrected', on the other hand, brings about a lot of tension. It is an attempt to outsmart the process of learning and evolution, this attempt itself is a kind of mistake. Pretending that there are no mistakes or that they don't need resolution doesn't work so well either. A mistake is still a mistake – it needs to be resolved but forcing this resolution with too much pressure can create more problems. We have to explore the limits of these polarities: try forcing from time to time, try ignoring from time to time. But we can explore the limits in a way that orients us to their connection through the space of the centre. A change of approach is needed.

Our centred option is to simply bear witness to the mistake and see it completely *as a mistake*; something that needs to be resolved at some point. If it continues, it is simply a case that the entirety of the mistake has not been seen – not a problem, we just need to continue our search with our practice. Being aware of an issue and believing that it isn't an issue or doesn't need to resolve means that on some level, you *want* to have that particular problem. In this case, it will not be resolved until you stop wanting it. This will happen when you can see the full extent of the problems you are causing to yourself and others around you by indulging in the behaviour. Once seen completely and fully, it will rectify itself (in time) without the need for any force. To know the mistake thoroughly, it is critical to live and experience the mistake for some amount of time; only this way can we become intimate enough to see it through to the root.

The discovery of any mistake is not something that needs to irritate us. On the contrary, its first appearance can be celebrated as finding it is the hard part; once seen, it becomes almost inevitable that it will slowly resolve as long as we maintain awareness of it. Sometimes we may only find a symptom or piece of the mistake, and investigation reveals a larger problem we didn't realise was there earlier. We can treat it like a game and keep a cosmic sense of humour about it all, finding the various clues that may hint at the deeper mystery to be discovered. Going into this labyrinth is one of the complexities of our deceptively simple practices.

It is much like untangling a fine chain necklace. If we try to force it, the knots will only get tighter and make us more frustrated. Likewise, if we pretend the tangle isn't a problem, it may catch on things and snap the chain. The solution is to relax a little and slowly, gently pick at bits until a section comes loose and can be drawn out.

A Force of Habit

The polarised responses that I've talked about through this book are often deeply ingrained habits. Habits are processes that we introduce into our lives to make things easier. When we change gears by driving, we habitually shift the gear stick as we press the clutch with our foot in a particular way. As it continues to work the same way every time it becomes habitual and mechanical. Being mechanical (and therefore always the same), it will often fall out of our awareness and when it does, our capacity for choice, growth, expression of willpower and our aliveness is taken away. A person may be just as bad a driver as they were when they just got off their Learner's because they stopped paying attention. Much like clockwork or a maths equation solved by a computer, a habit works in the manner of, *if x happens, then y always happens*. While there are some habits that we need to live in society, such as the habit of associating a person with their name, the great majority are completely unnecessary. They are burned into us by our culture, ancestors and childhood. When left unchecked and out of awareness, they can make our lives increasingly mechanical and numb. One can easily lose an entire lifetime 'going through the motions' when too much of our routine has become habitual – a sure way to remove joy from our lives.

Through practice, we can put the spotlight on habits that we were previously unaware of. We notice that tension, motion and postures appear without our wanting them to, or even appear when we specifically ask them not to. These habits are a good place to start our new examination, as they are manifested and tangible. Less obvious are the emotional habits. Even more elusive are the habits of thought, but with practice we will be able to see these too. Enclosing our individual *three treasures* are the habits we are born into of culture, time and family. These seep into us from all sides and create hidden automation across our being.

A LEGION OF HABITUAL PERSONAS

A normal habit everyone has is to create personas that project an idea of what we think people want to see in us. Over time, we end up so absorbed in these personas that we forget who we really are. This habit creates a cast of characters that we pretend to be or have unknowingly been taught to be. Being habitual, the ones we pretend to be, these false personalities, are a kind of mechanical intelligence. We can create hundreds and even thousands of these characters and often they *actively don't want to be found out.*

We are often so invested in the characters we pretend to be

that it is impossible for another to point them out to us. Being confronted with this reality is a scary notion for everyone, and often it simply causes another character to be created to deal with the fear of the situation and the uncertainty of the real self.

Different traditions throughout history have directly or indirectly alluded to this phenomenon. In the Bible there is a scene where Jesus confronts a demon named Legion, who could be seen as a symbolic representation of this cast of characters we carry around with us:

Then Jesus asked him, "What is your name?"

"My name is Legion," he replied, "for we are many." And he begged Jesus again and again not to send them out of the area.
                                        Mark 5:9 & 5:10 (NIV)

The demon begs not to have all his characters 'sent away'. Jesus does it anyway (he casts them into a herd of pigs, which immediately run off a cliff and drown in the ocean) and Legion ends up as a whole being. The people who witnessed this became terrified that Jesus will also send their characters away:

When they came to Jesus, they saw the man who had been possessed by the legion of demons sitting there, clothed and in his right mind; and they were afraid.

Those who had seen it described what had happened to the demon-possessed man and also to the pigs. And the people began to beg Jesus to leave their region.
                                        Mark 5:15, 5:16 & 5:17 (NIV)

These characters seek the comfortable and familiar. They smother our capacity for complete expression of true individual being and spontaneous creation. The more we are bound by their spell, the more we march through much of our lives like a robot: predictable, mechanical, void of true freedom and afraid of mystery.

One way to help ourselves be freed of this mistake of habit is (like any mistake) to gently shine the light of our own awareness straight onto it, to see the false personality through and through, plainly and clearly for what it is in an intimate and caring way. We must keep the false personalities in the awareness while they are operating, or at least recognise it afterwards. *Know the habit*. They appeared for a reason and can slowly resolve themselves provided you do not allow them to creep back into the shadows of ignorance.

> *La plus belle des ruses du diable est de vous persuader qu'il n'existe pas. [The finest trick of the devil is to persuade you that he does not exist.]*
>
> ~Charles Baudelaire

INHERITED HABITS

You have these habits and make these characters because of an impossible number of interacting factors: the pull of powerful currents of the time you were born into, the accepted beliefs of society, the way your parents raised you, your ancestry; these and many other strains of universal habit bear down on you, on others around you and on the world with immense pressure from across time and space. You don't have much of a choice about most of it having happened, but you can choose to start doing something about it. From this perspective you might say there are only two real choices: to be swept away by inevitable mechanicalness or gather all the resources you can to break free of the current and make for the shore of the great unknown.

Although this may sound like an immense task—and it is pretty immense—it is no use to despair and struggle. To use a very Australian analogy, it is like being in the surf and getting caught in a rip tide. To fight against the ocean is folly. It will only end in exhaustion and drowning. Surf life savers are taught to swim with the rip out beyond the crashing waves, where the shore can be seen and then swim parallel to the coast. When they see the gap in the rip they swim back safely to land. Like the life savers watching the ocean for rip tides, it is critical to be aware of the currents and tides of habit. Though invisible to the untrained, they become glaringly obvious when you look for their subtle patterns.

Polarity Shift

A common response we can have to being confronted with the shadows of deep habit is the swing from one extreme polarity to its opposite. You can see this happen all over the world. Fat goes from being the worst thing for you to the best. Sugar swings in the opposite direction, now vilified and deemed 'bad'. One fad succeeds another which has fallen from grace to become the new devil. The world seen through this lens is black and white, things either good or bad, right or wrong. It is ignorant of the colour and paradox of simultaneous occurrence of opposites that happens in reality.

Sugar is just sugar, a sweet food that can really add flavour when used at the proper time. Many people would do well to eat less of it. Some would benefit greatly from chilling out and just eating the chocolate they so desperately want to eat. Training obsessively is just as neurotic as avoiding it altogether. Balance is not static, but a fluid undulation between the two extreme poles, expressed from the centre where the polarity is neither, but influenced by both at the same time.

We will see these swings often in our practice. A mistake is noticed, and we compensate by swinging to the opposite pole. This is sometimes necessary and is fine; as we improve our awareness of such things, we can watch it unfold and know that it will come back to the centre or give it a little push if it doesn't. Often, we will find an aspect of ourselves that has been suppressed for many years and it can feel extraordinary to finally let it out. This can lead to a period of the opposite of suppression: indulgence. And when we find those things that we indulge in addictively, we can swing to the opposing camp of suppressing them. It is surprising how often we can swing but end up just as stuck as we were before, only now in the opposing camp.

This pattern can be seen often in practices of emotional trauma release therapy. A past issue is brought out of suppression and into awareness. The release feels wonderful, and often the person gets stuck in an addictive habit of finding suppressed traumas and bringing them out so they can indulge in the raw feelings of emotions that they blocked in themselves for so long. Whether the original issue being treated is resolved or not (often it is just re-lived and not resolved), the indulgence in the process can create a new array of issues.

A more physical example of my own illustrates my point further: I spent many years rarely going barefoot outdoors. When I realised what this mistake was doing to my feet, I spent the good part of a year, including most of winter, bare-foot everywhere I could – from the harsh outdoors to fancy restaurants! As far as my feet were concerned, it was excellent: they became much more alive and robust. At the same time, I brought unnecessary tension into many parts of my life. I created conflict with those who did not appreciate me dragging my bare dirty feet everywhere.

These days I choose my footwear to suit the context or how I feel. It's a much more relaxed and less forced expression of the entire spectrum between shod and not. In some cases, it is possible to come to this kind of balance without the need for the polarity swing. Doing this takes a level of skill that won't be available without practice. You must overcorrect at least a little to recognise what is 'too far'. Only then can you straddle the midline perfectly. If you do this enough, however, you might find that there is only one centre, and it is the same centre no matter what the context is.

It is also worth noting that different people will need a different frequency and amplitude of balance shift between poles. Just because a particular balance works well for you does not mean it will be suitable for the next person.

> *The shoe that fits one person pinches another; there is no recipe for living that suits all cases.*
>
> ~C.G. Jung

We can and should certainly learn from the mistakes of others, but do not for one second assume that because it did well for them, it will be equally virtuous for us. It is often the case that one person's mistake is another's medicine. We will each need to correct our own imbalances in an individual way. Guidance from an experienced teacher is sometimes crucial in this process.

THROWING OUT THE BABY WITH THE BATH WATER

A more subtle way that this polarity shift operates is in our relationships with other people. Gold can be found in the most obscure places and if you dismiss certain people because they do horrible or stupid things then you can close the potential for many wonderful opportunities to take form. Our culture often suggests that if a person is not smart, then they must be stupid, or that a person who does an extraordinarily cruel thing is not capable of compassion and love and doing good in the world. The paradox is that stupid people can say stupid things that are incredibly smart. Smart people can say smart things that are incredibly stupid. To be caught in the swing is to assume one or the other and not be able to see both qualities occurring simultaneously in different manifestations from the advantage of the mid-point.

When we look with clarity at polarised views, we will often see the same pattern repeating with an opposing polarity on the external face. Fundamentalist religious people are following the same patterns as hardcore scientific atheists. As are vegans and paleo-ites and opposing political parties. Take the same pattern, replace keywords with their opposing idea and *voilà*! When you begin to see the current of the pattern and not the surface façade, you will see that both sides are repeating a learnt habitual response, programmed with the same code. They have only switched the words and concepts.

We aim not to simply change from being the blue robot to the red robot, but to free ourselves completely from mechanisation, from being habitually stuck as one or the other. The opposites *are not separate*. They are the two ends of the same spectrum, two sides of the same coin, and they rely completely on each other. Both ends have their strengths and weaknesses, and there are always appropriate times to consider both extremes and act from those particular perspectives. To be alive is to be *whole*, to be free is to have all options available, to be wise is to use any given option *at the correct time*.

The Mirror

People stuck in these polarised views will often be irritated by their opposing camp. Any time you see something or someone that agitates you in some way, it is a clue for your personal development. The world we perceive reflects our agitations back to us. If you are agitated by the behaviour of another, you are either yourself indulging in a behaviour that follows the same pattern *or* suppressing the idea that you could be capable of such things. When you find this pattern in yourself, and resolve it, you will suddenly find that seeing others behave in this way no longer agitates you. Instead, you will see the person doing the pattern clearly—'Oh there they go again doing that thing'— without any agitation on your side, but now with a compassion that stems from knowing what it's like to be caught in such things. If you need to act in response to their behaviour, you will, but the internal or external complaint about the behaviour will cease.

There are obvious expressions of this law that are easier to work with in the beginning. People who are irritated by bad drivers tend to drive poorly themselves; people who are irritated by judgemental people are themselves extremely judgemental; people who are constantly talking about how poorly others are training are insecure with their own practice and so on. Seeing oneself in the reflection for the first time is a very vulnerable moment that requires a brutal sincerity. We have only ever been complaining about and agitated by ourselves, mostly the parts of ourselves that we don't want to admit are there. To confess our sins and repent in this manner is a truly holy undertaking. It is not about confessing to the other, it is about confessing to *yourself.* Sometimes admitting this out loud can be of enormous help.

More difficult to work with are the subtle patterns of suppression. These are different to the external expressions that can be witnessed and can require a significant amount of searching through the labyrinth to find completely. For example, it is often the case that people are agitated by others' aggressive behaviour. Believing themselves to never be aggressive, these people may not express direct aggressive behaviour, but it lurks in the shadows. Out of direct sight, it expresses instead in passive aggressiveness: complaining behind people's backs, internalising aggression through endless imagined conflicts (where they are always the victor, of course), or asserting their opinions too strongly in speech.

This particular example is a personal one and its discovery was quite monumental: *I get very angry sometimes!* But I would put on a character that pretended not to be angry because I was the guy doing self-cultivation and we aren't meant to get angry. I unconsciously pushed it down, away somewhere out of sight. This character of mine that pretended not to be angry was in conflict with reality, a reality which was desperately trying to show itself by reflecting my agitation when I saw other angry people. The reality of being a human is that we *all* have the positive parts and the negative parts as potential within us. To be whole within yourself is to see both sides of this. It can often be seen as contradictory or hypocritical to accommodate opposing forces. But to be human is to be *vast*.

> *Do I contradict myself?*
> *Very well then, I contradict myself;*
> *I am large, I contain multitudes.*
> ~Walt Whitman

The wonderful thing about the mirror is that it functions as a way of finding the issue and gives a very clear indication when a problematic pattern has been resolved. There is a not-so-subtle lightness that becomes obvious the first time you witness a former irritant after resolving the pattern – a very clear putting down of a burden. You see something that was previously bothersome, frustrating, or angering but those reactions no longer arise. Instead you see it and it just *is*. Not having a habitual reaction opens the possibility for an infinitude of other reactions, and often a great sense of intimacy with the moment as it happens.

START IN THE SHALLOW END

The mirror is an exceptionally useful tool for our development, but we need not start by peering into the most extreme depths of our mental and emotional habits to begin our practice. It is far too daunting to look at such things in any detail until one has built sufficient energy to do so. We can begin instead by taking the easily digestible: the physical habits. The physical is where we will begin to grow a capacity to cultivate the less confronting habits and it will naturally spread upward from there.

For this work we are primarily interested in physical habits of holding tension, motion and posture. If I tell you to relax your shoulders right now and you try and they become more relaxed, then you are holding unnecessary tension habitually. Are you able to lift your arm over your head without habitually engaging the trapezius muscle? We could also try relaxing the diaphragm, or the abdominals, and feel it relax to a deeper state than it was moments before, despite no change in the environment or no action performed. These are temporary effects that will fall away as soon as you stop thinking about them and the unconscious takes the reins again. This is why we have exercises like the ones shared in this book that need to be practised for long periods of time: to train the unconscious and prevent the tension from returning. As you work on these, you will also notice the mirror principle in effect: you will clearly see all the people around who are holding the same tension. When it stops being so obviously highlighted in the other (even if they haven't resolved the tension), it's a good sign that you're getting to the bottom of the issue in your own body.

Even though the physical is the most easily digested and where the majority of our first changes will appear, it is still prudent to prepare for the confrontations in the emotional and mental realms that will inevitably occur – this preparation comes from training all three treasures in equal measure from the beginning. I have, on many occasions, heard people talk about how the body and mind are linked and that if you are relaxed in the body you will be relaxed in the mind and vice versa and therefore you only need to train one or the other. In my observations, this is not completely true: the link between body and mind must be created through training. If there is a disconnect between the mind and body, if Yang and Yin are not linked through their centre, it will not work. As the union between the three treasures strengthens, the effect on the mind when you change the body (or on your body when you work on your mind) becomes more powerful. Without this union, you can make radical shifts in physical capacity and have almost no change to the mind, breathing or habitual layers and in some cases can drive certain habits deeper into your being.

It is very easy to find people with incredible physical capacity who have almost zero development of the mental qualities, or unstable emotional and breathing patterns. There are also plenty of high-level meditators whose bodies are weak and sickly. If training one always trained the other then these people wouldn't exist. It's not that there's anything particularly wrong with any of these situations, but if we want to develop our centring, we have to remember our mind can deceive us. It doesn't want us to engage with whichever aspect is going to pull the neat view of duality out from under it and so will come up with a thousand reasons why you don't need to do that part of your training.

Chapter 4:

Bringing It All Together

....

coagulate
[koh-ag-yuh-leyt; adjective koh-ag-yuh-lit, -leyt]

verb (used with or without object), co·ag·u·lat·ed,
co·ag·u·lat·ing.

- *to change from a fluid into a thickened mass;
  curdle; congeal*

- *bringing dispersed elements into an integrated
  whole, representing a new synthesis*

- *to gather or form into a mass or group.*

Developing a Personal Practice

I want to take some time now to bring everything together and give you an example of what a personal practice may look like.

We end up with two major parts of a practice: the formal parts where we dedicate specific time out of our day, and the informal parts where we do things *while* we are going about our normal life.

For the formal parts, the first thing to do is to build a habit of daily practice: without this nothing else can grow. We want to start with a very small and easy to accomplish baseline, and I usually recommend starting with five to ten minutes of any exercise from this book that you really enjoy. It has to be something enjoyable because we will inevitably run into one of those days in life where we have things to do all day and we arrive home late at night and the last thing you want to do is half an hour of practice. But five minutes of something you really enjoy can be accomplished no matter what, and the times where you do this after a hard day make a big difference in the long run.

Once you have established a habit of five to ten minutes a day and it's working well, it's now time to take care of your three treasures. Try adding one or two more five to ten-minute periods to what you are already doing. You will end up with three periods and, as discussed, we want to use one for doing something physical, one for doing some breathing or qi gong and one for training the mind. This book has included exercises from all three categories so if you are unsure just pick one of each that appeals to you. You can think of these three periods like slots that you tag exercises in and out of.

The informal parts, on the other hand, are just short moments scattered throughout the day. They are moments to become conscious of our habits and actions, or to do a small practice instead of being idle or unnecessarily distracted. We are waiting for the lift and instead of getting our phone out and checking social media, we just focus on a small point on the wall for thirty seconds, a mini version of the Red Ball drill. Or we interrupt someone telling a story and notice that we have a habit of interrupting (and also that people interrupting us really agitates us), celebrating that we've spotted a habit that we hadn't seen before. We are walking to the shops and decide to take a good posture, instead of habitually slouching, and walk while paying attention to our breath for three or four breath cycles. You could easily accommodate the formal or conceptual ideas throughout the day to make the informal part of practice start to cook. This will also allow our practice to start integrating into our lives a little more easily.

In Da Xuan we have a great qi gong practice where we increase the sensations in our hand, using specific postures and hand motions to train the quality formally. When I was first introduced to it, I also spent a good deal of time informally trying to increase the feeling in my hands (while I walked, for instance), using the same intention but without postures or motions used in the formal training. Playing around with the practices like this was never quite as powerful as when I practised the form, but I did it regularly and it definitely taught me a lot about the *quality* outside of the confines of the special set, which helped the quality grow. It also kept me in the present and in my body rather than lost in thoughts of past and future. These days, it takes just a moment to tune into the feeling of my hands and the sensation starts to increase no matter what I am doing – it is even working as I type this sentence!

Let's look at a fictional example of how these formal and informal practices work together:

John has spent two months practising his favourite exercise, conscious breathing, daily for five minutes. He's now feeling ready to increase his training. He is already doing five minutes of breathing, so he adds five minutes of staring at the red ball and five minutes of uncoupling the waist to his daily routine. He finds the uncoupling is best when he wakes up and attends to his conscious breathing and red ball in the evening, one after the other.

After another month of this routine, he's wanting a change from the conscious breathing, so he drops that. In its place he puts five minutes of his favourite qi gong exercise: static postures.

A few months later he's really enjoying the results of his training and so decides to increase the time he spends. He ups his time to 15 minutes of each category. His physical training now expands so he decides to continue the five minutes of the waist uncoupling and follow with ten minutes of pressing the back into the ground. For the qi gong and the red ball, he simply does the same exercises for longer periods of time.

Another two months go by and he changes it up again. The red ball gets tagged out for the yes method (15 minutes of mental work), the qi gong gets tagged out for abdominal breathing (15 minutes breathing), and he chooses three new physical exercises to do for five minutes each, back to back (15 minutes physical).

His daily routine is now 45 minutes, but he has a really crazy day where there is no chance of doing his practice. He arrives home at 3am, exhausted. He decides to just do five minutes of conscious breathing as he did when he started. The conscious breathing wakes him up a little so he decides to do a bit of his favourite physical exercise too, just five minutes. He is still too tired to focus so goes to bed, still having done ten minutes of practice. He missed his mental exercise but did a few informal focus exercises throughout the day for thirty to sixty seconds each so feels good about achieving something. The next day, having not been defeated by his busy day, he returns to his normal 45-minute routine.

This is just an example and obviously you want to structure your training in a way that works for you. But if you take the three treasures idea and the thresholds idea (I would say at least five minutes straight on any given exercise and try to stick to the same exercise for at least thirty days straight) then you can easily build your own practice. It's also worthwhile exploring longer stretches of training single exercises such as six and 12 months. You don't even have to use these techniques. You could very well try a run for your physical, some kind of yoga for your breathing and any kind of non-breathing meditation for your mental work.

At some point, if you want to delve deeper into this kind of work, you'll need a teacher and guidance from a tried and tested method or tradition. The Da Xuan tradition shines because it has over 1,500 years of experience and the guardians of the tradition were smart enough to continually adapt it to modern times, refining it to work for everyone today. It also has such a vast array of exercises to do for each of the three treasures that you are never stuck doing the same exercise for long unless you want to stay with it. The ideas and the exercises are quite simple – the secret lies in showing up for training every day! We must start somewhere and what better time to start than right now? As *Laozi* observed in the *Dao De Jing*:

A tree as great as a man's embrace springs up from a small shoot;
A terrace nine stories high begins with a pile of earth;
A journey of a thousand miles starts under one's feet.

Final Thoughts

When I first watched the interview series with Joseph Campbell, *The Power of the Myth*, I was deeply moved by his response to a question asking why anyone should care: 'Why myths? Why should we care about myths? What do they have to do with my life?' to which Joseph replied:

> *Well, my first answer would be, well, go on, live your life, it's a good life, you don't need this. I don't believe in being interested in subjects because they're said to be important and interesting. I believe in being caught by it somehow or other. But you may find that with a proper introduction, this subject will catch you. And so what can it do for you when it does catch you?*

This sentiment is echoed by the bygone masters of Da Xuan, who, if they were pressed for an answer to the question, 'Why should we do this?' would simply answer 'Don't'. I have tried to keep this as my operating motto in everything I do. I am far less interested in *convincing* people to do this kind of training and far more interested in giving it a proper introduction by presenting what I do as clearly as I can. It's my way of being of service by illuminating an option that may not have been known about; my way of opening the potential for others. Whether that potential is realised or not is not my business — it's up to you.

My hope is that this book provides a proper introduction to a subject which has grown to become my life's work and my deep passion. If you find yourself, as I was, caught by this approach and wanting to engage with this path, one thing stands out of everything I have written and all the things that you will practise: the simple idea that you should enjoy yourself. It takes a little time to get to this point as the start is confusing and overwhelming. Remind yourself regularly that you're *choosing* to train to improve your relationship with yourself and your life. You're not being forced to engage in a loveless labour, nor are you building a prison of exercises to isolate yourself from the difficulties of life. Don't waste so much time trying to figure out the processes, trying to 'know' or worrying if you're doing it 'correctly' or not. Just relax and get on with your practice and talk to your teacher if you are confused. If you miss some practice, don't stress ... just start it up again. Smile when you practise. Enjoy it, enjoy the changes it will bring, and enjoy your simplified life.

Happy training!

Figure 16 — Da Xuan logo

About the Author

....

Craig Mallett is an instructor and student of the Daoist tradition called Ba Men Da Xuan, under the direct tutelage of Serge Augier. Before committing to the tradition, he spent more than a decade seeking out and learning from the best teachers in the fields of physical development and self-cultivation. He has taught workshops on topics of natural movement, body awakening, stretching, and physical development from a Chinese Martial Arts perspective, across more than 20 cities throughout Europe and Australia. In his workshops and classes, Craig presents to beginners, casual practitioners, professional therapists, athletes and educators alike. His initial teachings and explorations were presented under the handle *Aware Relaxed Connected*, before he finally turned to the exclusive study and teaching practices of the Da Xuan tradition.

In 2017, with the permission of Serge Augier, he formally opened the Da Xuan school of Sydney, Australia. In 2019, he moved, along with the school, to Brisbane where he continues to further his studies while teaching practices from the Da Xuan tradition to local classes, online students, and in workshop formats around Australia and the world.

Further Reading & Resources

If you're interested in learning more about this approach or any of this work, please head over to Craig's website. There you will find information about possibilities of joining classes, workshops, online training, ways of contacting the author, and much more.

www.craigmallett.com

To learn more about the Da Xuan tradition of Daoism, please visit the website of Mr Serge Augier.

www.sergeaugier.com

Glossary

....

Always remember: *The menu is not the food. You can't eat the menu.* Knowing these terms and being able to discuss them intellectually won't improve your training in any way. As my teacher Serge has said to me on many occasions: 'The dao that can be talked about is not the actual dao, so you may as well shut up and train.'

That being said, here are some terms for your reference and curiosity:

bā mén dà xuán — 八门大玄
The name of my Daoist tradition. Literally translates to 'Eight Gates Big Mystery'.

chā quán — 查拳
Chā is a family name (properly written in pinyin as Zhā, however the alternative spelling has become more popular). **Quán** literally means fist, but is also translated as boxing (as in a boxing style). A traditional martial art style developed by the Hui Chinese. It is the predecessor to 長拳 **cháng quán** (literally: Long Fist), which is the central style used in modern **wǔshù** tournaments.

dān — 丹

Literally translated as Cinnabar or elixir. It refers to the alchemical process. Can be used as a suffix of many terms, e.g. **shéndān** (alchemy of the spirit), **nèidān** (internal alchemy), **wàidān** (external alchemy).

dào — 道

Way, road, path, method. In Daoism, refers to the way of all things. Commonly also written *'Tao'* as per the Wade-Giles romanisation system.

dàodé jīng — 道德经

The classic (**jīng**) of the way (**dào**) and its manifestations (**dé**). A fundamental classical Chinese text that all schools of Daoism refer to. Commonly also written as *'Tao Te Ching'* as per the Wade-Giles romanisation system.

fāngshì — 方士

Literally translated as Method Master, but has also been translated into English as wizard, sorcerer, magician, alchemist, shaman, medicine man and so on.

gōng — 功

Work, train, cultivate. Can be used as a suffix of many terms, e.g. **shéngōng** (to train the mind/spirit), **qìgōng** (to train the breath/energy), **nèigōng** (internal training, more or less the same meaning as **qìgōng**), **wàigōng** (external training), etc.

huízú — 回族

An ethnic group of people within China. Most of the Hui people are of the Islamic faith.

hùndùn — 混沌
The state of the universe/life before it separated itself into opposites.

jīng — 精
Essence, the material basis for the physical body.

lăozi — 老子
The name of the reputed author of **_dàodé jīng._** Also written in English as Lao Tsu, the name is actually an honorific title that literally means 'old master'.

nèi — 内
Inside, inner, internal.

pāidă — 拍打
Literally means slapping or patting. Refers to a Chinese practice of lightly slapping all surfaces of the body to increase circulation and promote health.

_qì_ — 氣
Energy, vitality, vital force, breath.

sānbăo - 三寶
Three jewels, three treasures. Refers specifically to the trinity of **_jīng_**, **_qì_** and **_shén_**. The trinity pattern is also sometimes deified and referred to as 三清, _sānqīng – the three pure ones._ For simplicity, I have used the term three treasures to refer to any instance of the trinity.

shén — 神
Mind, psyche, spirit, deity, soul, God.

tàijí — 太極
Oneness, supreme ultimate. Literally translates to 'great pole'.

tàijítú — 太極圖
A diagram depicting Yin and Yang mixing inside a circle. Colloquially referred to as the *'Yin Yang Symbol'* in English.

wài — 外
Outside, outer, external.

wújí — 无极
Infinite, limitless, emptiness, nothingness. Literally translates to 'without pole'.

wànwù — 万物
Everything, all. Literally translates to '10,000 things'.

wǔshù — 武术
Literally translated as martial (**wǔ**) arts (**shù**). In modern times it has been taken to almost exclusively refer to the modern style of demonstration martial arts, where participants compete in a gymnastics-style presentation and judges score the presentation based on a pre-defined set of rules.

xīn yì liù hé quán — 心意六和拳
Heart (**xīn**), Mind (**yì**) and Six (**liù**) Harmonies (**hé**) boxing (**quán**). A martial art style developed by the Hui Chinese. The concept of six harmonies also appears in many other Chinese martial styles.

yì — 意
Intent, thought, idea. Can refer to the process of thinking.

yīn & yáng — 陰陽
Literally translated as 'Dark (yin)/Bright(yang)' or 'Negative(yin)/Positive(yang)'. General terms to classify and compare opposing forces or ideas.

CPSIA information can be obtained
at www.ICGtesting.com
Printed in the USA
LVHW012337180720
661024LV00004B/149

9 780648 856603